TALES FROM THE GUNROOM

TALES FROM THE GUNROOM

Michael Paulet

Illustrations by Sally Townsend

WHARNCLIFFE PUBLISHING LIMITED

First published in 1994 by
Wharncliffe Publishing Limited
47 Church Street, Barnsley
South Yorkshire S70 2AS

A CIP catalogue record for this book is available from the British Library

ISBN 1 871647 21 5

For up-to-date information about other titles produced under the Wharncliffe
Publishing imprint, please telephone or write to:

Wharncliffe Publishing Limited
FREEPOST
47 Church Street
Barnsley
South Yorkshire S70 2BR

Telephone no. (24 hours): (0226) 734555

Typeset by Yorkshire Web in Plantin 11 point

Printed in Great Britain by
Redwood Books,
Trowbridge, Wiltshire

CONTENTS

Chapter One

Stuffy Brewster

Arthur Brewster and I were at school together, and met one another again in the Army, though we did not serve in the same regiment. He retired from the service to run an estate in Lincolnshire left to him by his uncle. He was not a companionable man in the sense of being happy in boisterous company, and this, perhaps undeservedly, had earned him his nickname. He was not much good at small talk, and was terrified of women whom he regarded as fast. His outward appearance of unsociability was redeemed by a deep-rooted affection for people who gained his friendship. He also possessed that most effective sense of humour, a dry one.

Stuffy Brewster and I were having dinner together. Usually when he came up to London – which was not often – he would give me a ring and we would dine, either at his club or mine, depending on whose turn it was to do the honours. On this occasion it was mine.

The dining room of a gentleman's club in London is a statement of established values: orderliness; lack of ostentation; no undue haste; no raised voices; no rustling exchange of documents – just a temperate buzz of conversation. Club servants (not waiters) going their rounds from table to table – linen, glass and silver – bearing their offering of country-house dishes, not an epicurean feast, but food and wine to suit the taste of members and their guests.

Sooner or later during our dinners together Stuffy and I would get on to the subject of shooting. That was largely the purpose of them, so far as he was concerned anyway.

It was early in August, and newspaper editors short of news had been filling in with the usual ill-informed tittle-tattle about 'The Glorious Twelfth'. I read in one paper that a certain peer had once lost an eye in a shooting accident while "Potting grouse near Newmarket" and a one-eyed racehorse had been named after him. I remembered the comment that went the rounds a few years earlier when an unpopular sportsman maimed his equally unpopular host in the same way. 'Shit shot shit' was the caustic quip.

I asked Stuffy if he had noticed the piece I had read in the morning papers.

'Yes,' he said. He paused whilst our plates were removed, then fell serious.

'Harry,' he said, 'does it ever strike you how much shooting has changed since you and I bagged our first pheasant? I sometimes wonder if we aren't just a couple of old die-hards living in the past. And yet when I read about guaranteed bags, or tame birds being shoved into the coverts half-way through the season to top up, I begin to wonder what motivates some of the people who shoot these days. We did after all learn to enjoy our shooting because we served an apprenticeship and understood our craft; if some of us were more skilful at it than others, what matter! Besides, each of us has his own little triumphs to remember. Sport, that's what it's supposed to be, not a game to win. From what I see and hear, a good many people think differently these days.'

'To be fair, a great many of today's shooters didn't get it handed to them on a plate like we did,' I said. 'They took up shooting when the opportunity arose, and they started from scratch: buy a gun, learn to use it, find somewhere to shoot, and shoot more than the other fellows. Who was there to guide them otherwise? It's as if the competitiveness of clay shooting has infiltrated the ethics of game shooting. In my opinion there are plenty of people who shoot now — both young and old — who are on the right lines; they shoot because they want to enjoy themselves, not because they want to win. I'm afraid, though, there are too many people about who have taken up shooting with the will to win: win by shooting more birds, win by doing something Jones doesn't, win contracts and win clients. I read the other day that one City company alone spends £300,000 on shooting for their clients. They reckon it brings them in £30 millions' worth of business.'

'If I had my time again, I swear to you, Harry, I wouldn't shoot for anything other than pleasure. I admit I have been lucky enough to have my own shoot, and be able to ask my friends. But, as you know, it hasn't always been like that. There was a time when I had nothing to offer in exchange, and still I have had the best of sport. Sometimes with a bit of effort and a tongue in my head I have found it for myself. Frequently it was offered to me subject only to my safety, good manners, provision of cartridges, and a tip for the keeper. I have accepted with gratitude, which was all that was asked of me.'

'In that respect things certainly have changed,' I said. 'The other day a fellow I know said he was sorry he hadn't been able to fit me in again this season, all his guest days were taken up by business associates or people who asked him to shoot. Slightly embarrassed, I muttered something about being sorry that I hadn't any shooting of my own to offer in return. "You mean you accepted my invitation when you couldn't reciprocate?" he replied, as if he'd been stung.'

Stuffy picked up his half-empty glass of port, gazed reflectively into the contents, and finished it off. 'I don't suppose it will be long before you can go into Harrods, produce your credit card, and order a day's pheasant shooting over the counter. Money back if you don't get the guaranteed bag. But I do wonder how young people ever get started these days.' He looked at his watch. 'Now look here, Harry, I really must be getting home,' he said. 'Thanks for a very nice dinner, I've enjoyed it a great deal. If they can get me a cab I'll be off now.'

Except for a brief letter thanking me for dinner, I did not hear again from Stuffy Brewster. I did not expect to, because he did not write letters. And except for an abrupt conversation to arrange something, he did not like the telephone either.

Over the past few years I have got into the habit of glancing through the obituary columns in the newspaper I read, not from the morbid curiosity of seeing if any of my contemporaries are featured, but for the gems some of them contain. One of my favourites is that of the Maharajah of Bikaner — a famous shot. His grandfather, the obituary records, was inordinately fond of shooting sand grouse, and was dubbed by a contemporary English wag, 'Prince of Bikaner, by the grouse of God'.

Some six weeks after my dinner with Stuffy Brewster I was looking through the obituaries in my morning paper, and had got to the bottom of the main columns, when my eye caught the following:

Major Arthur (Stuffy) Clarence Brewster, of Cranworth House, Flixby, Lincolnshire. Aged 70. Educated at Wellington College, and commissioned in 1935 into The Royal Artillery, he served throughout the war with The Royal Horse Artillery, winning the Military Cross at the Battle of Cassino. Arthur Brewster left the Army in 1950 to manage his late uncle's estate at Flixby. He was unmarried.

The 14th of January 1985 — the first of our Gunroom dinners. From where I sat at one end, I looked down the two lines of white shirt-fronts and black ties on either side of the long polished table, the soft light coming from the three candelabra spaced down the length of it, reflecting the features above the black bow ties. How we all came to be there I will explain shortly.

Most I recognised. Each face saying something or listening to something being said, each registering the range of expression associated with a group of people perfectly at ease talking amongst themselves. It struck me that here was a reunion without strings. There was no chairman to be chatted

4

up, no bore you had been at school with to hear reliving his triumphs in the First Eleven, no battles refought, no hardships relived. Just one common interest and one common friend. Stuffy would have been pleased.

I had worked out a seating plan beforehand, with no particular regard to personalities, but because it cuts short the hiatus whilst everyone sorts themselves out before sitting down, and when they do sit down it gets the conversation going right from the start. The steady buzz of talk, with an occasional peal of laughter, or one voice raised above the rest, had continued unabated. Now we had reached the final relaxation of coffee, smoking and liqueurs. In this mood of repletion, I noticed more listeners than talkers. It was the time for tales.

I had been allowing myself the privilege of a host, ignoring conversation to assess how well the party was going. The voice next door asking me a question relieved me of this privilege.

It was not really mine anyway. The privilege had been delegated to me by Stuffy Brewster.

By the time I got home from the City where we had held the dinner, my wife was already in bed asleep. There was no doubt the evening had been a success, mainly due to the company, partly due to the organisation. The most important feature of the organisation had been finding a suitable place, and Billy Clavering had come up trumps here, putting us in touch with a small City livery company. The room had been a pleasant mixture of elegance and intimacy, smallish, well-proportioned, with good prints on the panelled walls and an absence of heavy oil paintings of former dignitaries; the light diffused by wall-brackets instead of garishly reflected through crystal chandeliers, and you could hear other people talk without effort. The food and the wine had been simple but good.

Certainly we had enjoyed ourselves, but had we fulfilled the purpose that Arthur Brewster had in mind when he left money in his will, 'For my friends to dine together every

5

year and swap each other's stories'? It was uncharacteristic of him not to have a purpose when he set something in motion.

The following morning I felt rather flat. The planning, the organisation, the reunion of old shooting friends, the chat and the stories were all over. We would not forgather again for another year, and by then we would all have forgotten last year's dinner and last year's stories. Then an idea struck me. It was prompted by remembering a fat leather-bound book the size of a photograph album we had in the officers' mess when I was in the Army. Inscribed in gold letters on the cover were the words, Lie Book.

The purpose of this book was to keep a record of the lighter side of life in the Regiment, as seen by the officers. If something happened which was unusual and amusing, it was written up in the Lie Book. No one was either officially or unofficially responsible for writing an account of an incident: whoever chose to chronicle it did so there and then. As a result the entries were entirely spontaneous, and the reader got a feel for the mood of the moment.

Here was an idea, it struck me, which could be adapted to our newly formed Gunroom, to keep some written record of the better stories which were told at our dinners. It would be a chronicle, if not for posterity, then for our own amusement and maybe for our children's in years to come. It would also be a testimonial to the memory of Stuffy Brewster.

Shortly after his death, I went to Stuffy Brewster's memorial service, a modest affair arranged by his sister. I doubt if he would have wanted one himself. For the convenience of his friends it was held in a London church. As they settled down into their places, people nodded and smiled their quiet greetings. The service proceeded. Then as the organ played the opening bars of 'Abide With Me', I started to sing, but with a lump in my throat. I found it too difficult.

I wondered what epitaph, if any, his sister would choose to put on Arthur Brewster's gravestone. One which I have always remembered struck me as entirely appropriate, 'An upright downright honest man'.

But who am I, I who recall this about my late friend Arthur Brewster? Well, my name is Harry Agnew. I am of independent occupation and limited but adequate means, having served first the Army and then the family brewing firm. The Army provided me with much pleasure but a limited future; the family firm with less pleasure and an equally limited future, since it was taken over and I was made involuntarily redundant. So having served other people for most of my working life, I am at length responsible for serving only my conscience and my family. I have time on my hands.

A habit I have acquired with the years is to look at the postmarks of letters before opening them. I suppose it must have been a couple of months after Arthur Brewster's death when, in my mail one morning, a letter arrived with the postmark Lincoln. I knew no one who lived in Lincolnshire, except for Stuffy when he was alive. I opened the other envelopes first, then the one from Lincoln. The letter inside was from a firm of solicitors. It informed me that the late Major A. C. Brewster had left to me in his will the sum of five thousand pounds. 'We were instructed by the late Major Brewster to insert the following clause,' the letter continued: ' "It is my wish that this money be used for my friends to dine together every year and swap each other's stories." ' The solicitor was not going to leave it at that. 'Although we pointed out to Major Brewster the legal imprecision of this clause, he insisted that it be included, and that the beneficiary would clearly understand his wishes. In the circumstances...' And the letter went on to define a few.

Understanding Stuffy's wish was one thing, implementing it was another, and I settled on three longstanding friends to advise me: Mike Caldecott, a landowner, David Radford, a wine merchant, and Billy Clavering, an ex-Regular soldier whose apparently ample means of support I have yet to discover. They had all been friends of Arthur Brewster as well.

We met, and decided on the following general principles for what we decided to call 'The Gunroom'. We would hold a dinner at least once a year. If it could be conveniently arranged, we would hold it in the first half of January when the season of Christmas and the New Year was over, when we had all had some shooting days to talk about, and while there were a few more we could look forward to before the end of the season. We would ask our guests for no other reason than to enjoy themselves. We did not enter into any serious discussion over the issue of ladies being present.

Why the name Gunroom? You may even ask what is a gunroom, since there are very few people these days who have such a room in their house. It was not always so. In the days of boudoirs and libraries, the grander (or more pretentious) country houses also had a gunroom in which the master of the house stored his collection of sporting weaponry, cartridges, and other shooting paraphernalia. Whilst he contemplated his collection, he might feel the need of a little liquid refreshment, and so bottles, decanters and glasses would often find a home in one of the cupboards. Except for the cupboards, shelves and racks, the room was usually sparsely furnished with a table and a few chairs, not the place where the mistress of the house was likely to visit. Herein lay the other advantage of the room to the master of the house, for he could slip in there with a few friends, ostensibly to admire the guns and talk about shooting, and other things, undisturbed.

Therefore, although few people have them these days, gunrooms are synonymous with shooting stories. The name seemed an appropriate one to carry over into the late twentieth century for the group of Stuffy Brewster's friends and their guests, as they talked each year about shooting, and other things, undisturbed.

The Gunroom has been flourishing for ten years, and the book is already half-full of handwriting — mostly mine, since it falls to me to record the stories after each dinner.

The following chapters record the memories of men who have shot all their lives, and who love their sport. By preserving our memories I hope we will also preserve the sporting ethic that Stuffy Brewster − like all of us − so valued.

Chapter Two

But No More Like My Father

It had been a bitter cold day with north-easterly gales causing chaos on the roads and railways. The weather forecasters had failed to predict this vicious onslaught. Those of us – surprisingly, considering the conditions, most – who had made it to the Gunroom dinner that same evening were basking in the warmth and comfort of the room where we had met last year, the unpleasant journey forgotten in the afterglow of soup and sherry, roast grouse and claret, sorbet, and Stilton. And now port and coffee.

The grouse was excellent, but, as I remarked to my neighbour, it could not possibly have come from the moor owned by a friend of mine. He did not hit it off with his son at all; indeed, there was open warfare between them. The son had a lot of money in his own right, and knew that a piece of land adjoining his father's grouse moor was likely soon to come on the market. He slipped in a bid with nominees, and bought the land. That season, on a day in mid-August, when he knew that his father was shooting the part of the moor closest to his bit of land, he organised a pop concert. It was a matter of regret to everyone that the noise was so loud that my friend's comments, and those of his keeper, could not be heard.

Then Mike Caldecott spoke. 'I am not an authority on fathers,' he began, 'for mine was killed when I was ten years old. The absence of a guiding influence, or the lack of it, does, however, sharpen one's memory of the surrogates.'

Mike continued to speak, as he sensed our interest in his

10

story. 'When my father was killed my mother was left with very little money and two children, my younger sister and myself. We lived in a cottage on my grandfather's stud farm. I had never met my mother's father before, and I subsequently learnt that he did not approve of her marriage, and therefore presumably of me. My first, and almost only, recollection of him is being ushered into his presence, and seeing him sitting there in a high-backed chair with a Great Dane dog lying on the floor beside him, and a vast jigsaw puzzle on a card table in front of him. I cannot remember what he said to me then, or on any other occasion, neither can I remember him ever giving me a present of any kind.

'I have an original Spy cartoon of him now, in a brown Homburg hat, Harrovian tie, brown suit and shoes, race glasses slung round his neck, case suspended over right shoulder in the conventional crutch position. He looks as if his horse had just won the Derby. I also have his pair of guns, which my mother got her hands on somehow when he died.

'By all accounts my grandfather's 500-acre stud farm produced indifferent racehorses, but quite good wild pheasants. I remember being taken out shooting by my mother. My grandfather further disapproved of me when he found out that I was gunshy.

'My mother had inherited champagne tastes; but since her marriage had only been provided with a cider income. It was a situation she was determined to alter. She did so by marrying the owner of a prosperous brewery, a good deal older than herself. This enabled her to indulge her passion for racing, and in due course to introduce her children to the way of life she had been used to before marrying my impecunious father.

'My mother was determined that I should take up shooting (as she was that my sister should go hunting), but she had the problem of my gunshyness; in fact this had already been largely overcome, though I still tremble at big bangs. I was in my early teens, and my grandfather had by now gone to meet his maker; in any case, my mother probably recognised that it was most unlikely he would ever have taken on such

11

an unpromising shooting apprentice as his grandson. She therefore turned to a neighbouring landowner whom she hoped might be persuaded to teach me to shoot as a gentleman should. He had been a friend of my grandfather's, and his land marched with my grandfather's stud, now sold; his wife was one of my mother's racing cronies. I can imagine my mother, who worked hard for her children, saying how sad it was that I had no one now to teach me to shoot.

'That was how I came to become the protégé of Edward Lambert, Esquire, of Hinswell Manor in Suffolk, and to be placed under the tutelage of George Duke, his gamekeeper.

'Mr Lambert was a courtly old gentleman who exactly fitted the image of the old-fashioned squire. I saw him that way; it is the only way I can find to describe him. I use the word image, but to him I don't think for a moment it was an image, he was just living a life, a quiet, stable, well-ordered life that was natural to his class and his generation. He and his wife had no son or daughter of their own, and I think he, especially, came to regard me as the only possible substitute in the circumstances. He did not just hand me over to Duke his gamekeeper; he made sure I was safe to be handed over first. Neither did he neglect me when I had been handed over, for he often took me out walking with a gun himself, and later I was allowed to stand in the line with the other guns, his guests, when there was a proper shoot.

'It is often the case, isn't it, that the young find it easier going with one of the retainers than it is with the master. And so I found it with Duke and Mr Lambert. Age and formality all imposed their barriers up at the Manor; the butler opening the door, announcing the presence of a fifteen year-old boy, and leaving him alone with the grey-haired man in the plus-four suit. The three-course lunch and the polite conversation. The walk with our guns afterwards, Mr Lambert and myself. Then tea: China or Indian, toast or sandwiches, and cakes; politeness just one jump ahead of gluttony.

'Duke must have been in his early sixties when I first knew

him. He had fought in the Great War and been severely wounded, which accounted for his unusual appearance. He had apparently been hit in the face by something, either a bullet or a shell splinter, and as a result lost the greater part of his nose. The damage had been repaired by removing a piece of one of his rib-bones, implanting it where the nose ought to be, and grafting over the makeshift nose-bone a piece of skin removed from his forehead. The remodelling of Duke's face, the oddly shaped nose, and the white patch on one side of his forehead where the surgeons had removed the skin for the graft, made him look like a disfigured and rather aged teddy bear. His white hair grew in what used to be called a cow-lick, a tuft of hair in the front which does not lie in the same direction as the rest of the hair. He always spoke as if he had got a bit of a cold; no wonder, with a reconstituted nose.

'I never saw Duke dressed in other than a pair of full-cut breeches, which narrowed over the knee to button at the side beneath and tuck into a pair of drab-coloured woollen stockings. His feet were usually encased in leather lace-up boots; I never saw him wearing gum-boots, though doubtless he did wear them on occasions. Outside, he wore a shapeless full-skirted coat with a single slit at the back to allow for two large poacher's pockets, one on either side. On his head — he never went outside without it — he wore a broadbrimmed felt hat. If I called to see him when he was inside his cottage, he was without hat and coat; carpet slippers had been substituted for boots, and he wore braces to keep up his breeches like the ones you see in old films of the US Cavalry.

'Mrs Duke was neat, grey, and tidy. She kept the inside of the cottage so tidy that even I noticed it.

'During the school holidays Duke became my constant companion. I like to think he enjoyed my company: I know I welcomed his more than the company of most other grown-up men with whom I came in contact. Whenever I could, I used to bicycle over to Hinswell, lean the bicycle against the wooden railings outside the keeper's cottage, and go round to the back. If I did not find Duke with his ferrets or dogs in the outbuildings, I would knock on the door of the cottage, and neat, tidy Mrs Duke would answer. "He's up at the Hundredacre" she might say. And off I would go to find him.

'For all the commonplace knowledge that I have acquired over the years about the habits of birds and beasts, for all the information I have picked up in forty years' shooting, there are things I remember which Duke told me that no-one has told me since.

'"Yew never want to ride a bike" Duke said, "with an owd hare a hangin' from the handlebars, the head'll git caught in the spokes. A rabbit's orl right 'cause that ain't long enough fer the head to git caught." Useless information nowadays maybe, but practical common sense then. Another thing he taught me — I've seldom seen it done since — was how to draw a woodcock's sinews. Quite the tastiest part of a woodcock to eat are its legs, but like most game birds the legs are threaded with tough sinews, and these can only be extracted easily when the bird is freshly killed. Duke showed me what to do. Wrap a handkerchief round the lower part of the shot bird's leg, break the leg at the knee-joint by twisting, and pull — hard. The scaly part of the leg comes away with the sinews attached. It works only if the bird is still warm when you do it. And how many people these days can find a woodcock's pin-feathers; even know what pin-feathers look like? Duke showed me where to find them.

'There was a hutch full of ferrets round the back of Duke's cottage. Out of curiosity I used to poke a four-ten cartridge through the wire mesh, and the ferrets would bite at it viciously; you could see the teeth marks right through to the shot. Some of his ferrets, usually the young ones, bit on sight if you were fool enough to present them with a biteable target, others were much tamer. You couldn't always tell which were which. Eventually I became brave enough to pick a ferret up the right way, and know that if I held it firmly the little beast could not get its head round sufficiently to nail me. I learnt to treat all ferrets with caution. There was one exception, a polecat line ferret which Duke gave to me.

'I remember the delight with which I received this gift, and bore the old buck ferret home with pride. I christened him Charlie. He lived in a hutch where he could neither be seen or smelt from the house. He was absolutely tame, and one of his great pleasures in life, now that he was no longer able to go hunting on his own, was to chase a rabbit's scut (tail) tied to a long piece of string. Having got his teeth into the fur and bone of the scut he would hang on like grim death, happy to be dragged along the ground or, like a whirling dervish, to become airborne.

'Before I was banished to eat elsewhere, one of my mother's guests at a dinner-party took an unaccustomed interest in my conversation. I soon turned to the subject of my ferret Charlie. I felt that just talking about Charlie really did not do him justice, he had to be seen to be appreciated. So I went and fetched him from his hutch at the end of the garden. Sadly, he was not appreciated.

'One year at Hinswell there were a lot of collar doves about; these birds looked to me only a little smaller than a pigeon, and much easier to shoot. I asked Duke if I could shoot them. He said, "I don't shoot a dove, that bring bad luck". He went on to explain that his first master had ordered him to shoot all the doves on the place he could, because they were becoming a nuisance. Duke did so and soon after his master went bankrupt. He had been told to do the same thing by another of his masters, and this time the man lost his wife; in what circumstances Duke did not specify.

'When you come to think of it, as well as being the symbol of peace, the dove was also used by Christian painters to symbolise the soul of the dead. An old gamekeeper's well-founded superstition (which I have neither heard of nor read about since) first stayed my youthful killer instinct; imagined supernatural retribution may have subsequently influenced me, but I have never shot a dove from that day to this.

'In those happy-go-lucky days all that seemed to matter was when the next term started. When I went to bed at night, I read all the books on shooting I could find. I wasn't so much interested in the technical stuff about guns; it was the nature of shooting that fired my imagination. I wanted to snuggle down sharing the author's experiences: meet as I dropped off to sleep the characters he wrote of, and pick up from him the lore about animals and birds.

'I liked best the books which sent me to sleep thinking about the characters in our East Anglian countryside, characters who had to do with Duke's world, now my own as well.

'Downstairs at home in the big bookcase in the hall were all the Badminton Library titles. A poacher, I read, is a cowardly drunken ruffian, with a suspicious leer, hollow eyes, and an alehouse face. I wondered what an alehouse face looked like. I wondered what Duke did about poachers. I did hear from him that the chairman of the local bench of magistrates, one Sir Christopher Rattray, was hot stuff on anyone caught poaching. He was also a large local landowner. Somehow I could not imagine Duke bringing one of these cowardly bearded ruffians, as illustrated in the book, in front of Sir Christopher. Maybe Duke's father had done so, not in front of Sir Christopher, but in front of one of Sir Christopher's predecessors.

'Then came the war. There are certain obvious things I can remember that were inconvenient, but to a boy living in the country the death and destruction, if he ever thought of war like that, seemed a long way off. Indeed, there was an air of excitement about what was happening. I don't think it ever occurred to me that we might actually lose, or that I might have to go and fight for my country. Not at this stage anyway. My grown-up step-brother, who I knew only by his occasional visits, went off to join the Territorial regiment which his father had commanded in the last war. We had a massive air-raid shelter dug in the garden; it was never used – except for growing mushrooms. The nearest bomb fell

16

three miles away, jettisoned – we were told – by a returning bomber.

'Duke too became involved in the second world war of his lifetime. He joined the Home Guard, and became platoon sergeant of the Hinswell Platoon. He took his duties very seriously, though he constantly complained to me – and no doubt to Mr Lambert as well – about the inroads the Home Guard made on his other duties as a gamekeeper. Not wishing to offend my sensitive young ears, he would refer to, "the humbuggerin' Hoome Guard" when explaining that there was duty to be done which meant that gamekeepering would have to take second place to the war effort.

'During those wartime summer holidays, I shot rabbits. I know the rabbit has made a comeback since myxomatosis, but the numbers cannot be as great as they were before the disease struck. I remember the main road just south of Brandon in Suffolk, where the tarmac was spattered with rabbits squashed by the traffic like so many flies on a flypaper.

'The Hinswell estate had big open fields of light sandy soil; ideal rabbit territory. And the best time of all for shooting the rabbits was during harvest.

'There were no combine harvesters then; the binder pulled by a tractor cut its way into the big fields of standing corn. I remember the continuous clack of the blades as they cut swathe after swathe round the field, and the regular sound of metal locking with metal to eject the bound sheaves of cut corn. As the standing crop diminished the rabbits began to bolt, first an occasional one, then, as the island which offered protection grew smaller, in increasing numbers until only a strip was left and the last inhabitants had to make a run for it across a wide sea of stubble.

'We stood with our guns at each corner of the uncut crop, twenty-five yards or so out on the stubble, and shot the rabbits as they bolted, usually managing – with the occasional miss – to roll them over cleanly. You had to be careful where you were shooting, but by now I had learnt to keep a cool head; one dangerous shot and I would have been sent straight home

– unthinkable! I'd rather let a rabbit by than take a chance.
A good form of discipline for an excited lad to learn safety out
shooting.

'A hundred rabbits and more, that's what we used to get
out of some of the bigger fields, and very much in demand
they were with the wartime meat shortage. What I did not like
was helping Duke to paunch them all afterwards.

'The Fall of France, Dunkirk, the Battle of Britain: I
listened to the cool voice of the BBC announcer as each crisis
built up, happened, and was overtaken by the next. I saw the
photographs of Britain at war in each day's papers, and in
Picture Post once a week. I bicycled to the local cinema, sat
in the one-and-sixpennies, and watched the scenes of battle
on Gaumont British News before the feature film. And having
listened and seen I forgot, and thought about tomorrow,
rabbit or pigeon shooting, and how many days were left before
I had to go back to school.

'Then, in early 1942, the war came closer to home with the
news that my step-father's only son had been killed when
Singapore fell to the Japanese. His battalion had formed part
of a division largely composed of East Anglian regiments who
were wiped out when the Japs attacked from the rear. I should
be able to recall the atmosphere at home after such a tragedy,
but for the life of me I cannot. I do remember, though, going
up to see Duke on one of my regular visits. He was not around
the back of the cottage so I knocked on the door; after several
moments it was opened to me by Mrs Duke. She did not look
at me and she did not say anything. I could see Duke in his
shirtsleeves and braces behind her. All he said was, "I think
you'd best go home today, Master Mike". I wondered if I had
done anything wrong.

'The time came when I too had to volunteer for one of the
Services or get conscripted. I chose to volunteer, which left
my options a little more open. At the beginning of the 1944
shooting season I joined the Army. And our lives, Duke's and
mine, began to grow apart.

'The memory of my days with Duke is so vivid that it is

difficult to explain why I can remember the beginning and not the end. I would expect to be able to say that my last memory of Duke was seeing him standing outside his cottage as I bicycled off one cold January day. But it is not the case. He just sort of faded from my life, as indistinctly as the memory of him is distinct. But there is a sequel.

'Years later I happened to meet the man who had been Mr Lambert's chauffeur at Hinswell, and we got talking about the old days. Did I know, he asked me, that Duke had a son, his only child? I did not. He went on to tell me that before the war Duke's son had run away and joined the Army. When war broke out he was commissioned, and was then reported missing believed killed after the fall of Singapore. Miraculously, after VJ Day, he was found alive in a hospital attached to a Japanese prisoner-of-war camp, and repatriated. "O' course owd George Duke and his missus is both dead now," said the chauffeur, "but I believe the son is teachin' science or suthin' at Cambridge University."

'Out of curiosity I looked up the name Duke under Cambridge in *The Universities Yearbook*. I found the entry. Briefly it read: "Duke, Dr P. J., Reader in Theoretical Physics".'

Chapter Three

Uncle Cyril

I remember very well the circumstances in which the next tale came to be told. The subject of conversation at dinner that evening had turned to the case, reported some days earlier in the newspapers, of the hot-air balloonist who claimed that his craft had been shot at by Lord Mountgarret as it crossed over the latter's grouse moor.

Someone round the table commented that peers seemed especially prone to the use of powder and shot as a method of expressing their feelings. It was not so very long ago, he recalled, that another noble lord got into trouble with the law for firing a cannon-ball across the Menai Straits and making a hole in the sail of a passing yacht.

Being a member of the House of Lords is not what it used to be, I thought. I remembered an apocryphal story about a farm worker in the last century who was shot by one of the guns. The man complained bitterly about his painful wound, only to be rebuked by his master, and told he ought to be proud. Did he not know that he had just been shot by the great Duke of Wellington!

Inheriting a title may no longer carry the same privileges and immunity that it once did; nevertheless being an English lord does, in the public view at least, entitle the holder to a certain amount of inherited eccentricity. An errant peer makes a prime target for a journalist when hard news is in short supply. Either you have the *White Mischief* scene (Sir Jock Delves Broughton was sent a cable by Lord Caernarvon after his acquittal: 'Hearty congratulations on winning by a neck cleverly'), or little indiscretions such as selecting a hot-air balloonist for a target, and firing cannon-balls from the battlements of your home. The British aristocracy seldom disappoints, and Billy Clavering's Uncle Cyril was cast in the right mould.

Billy began his story. 'I cannot say whether my Uncle Cyril ever actually fired a warning shot in someone's direction, but if he did, it was likely to be a pretty close call for whoever it was that caused him to do so. My uncle is Lord St Helens, and he is very conscious of his rank and dignity. He has also got a filthy temper. Uncle Cyril's place, as he calls it, is Clatworth on the Lancashire coast. The estate has been in the family for generations; he manages to keep it going by selling things, land and pictures mostly. The Clatworth estate does have one considerable asset though. The sea is gradually receding on that part of the coast, so Uncle Cyril gains a bit of land each year as well as selling some.

'There is a shoot at Clatworth, quite a good shoot, but it suffers from two major disadvantages: a lack of investment in pheasants and the corn to feed them, and a rapid turnover in gamekeepers. The wild birds don't find the sea air on that part of the coast especially invigorating and their natural diet is restricted; for shooting purposes their numbers have to be supplemented by a considerable influx from the rearing pens. Once out in the coverts the pheasants have to be persuaded to stay there with a liberal supply of corn, otherwise they are forced by necessity to go wandering in search of food. Uncle Cyril strikes a nice balance between the interests of ecology and economy − as he sees it. The human factor, namely a reliable gamekeeper in residence, is a recurrent problem at Clatworth. The last man, Blackall, took Uncle Cyril to an industrial tribunal claiming wrongful dismissal.

'It happened like this. Blackall was a blunt Yorkshireman who had spent the first twelve years of his life in the Army before turning to keepering, and he was used to calling his superiors "Sir" with no other embellishment. Uncle Cyril bluntly told him that he should be addressed as "My Lord".

21

Blackall said he only knew of one lord he would be called upon to address in that manner and that was the Lord Above. Thankfully he had not yet made his acquaintance. "Ah'm a gamekeeper, not a lackey," was a remark Uncle Cyril did not appreciate.

'A bad beginning. Blackall was as good as his word; he was liberal enough with his "Sirs" but that was as far as it went. Blunt Blackall may have been, but by all accounts he was a good and conscientious gamekeeper and, to be fair, my uncle seemed to appreciate this. All went well for a time, then there was the matter of a disagreement between them over the amount of corn fed to the pheasants. The keeper, taken to task very abruptly over the amount of the last feed bill, retorted something like, "Tha can't feed bloody birds on booger all," and registered another totted-up penalty point with Uncle Cyril.

'The third offence was Blackall's last in my uncle's employment; it happened on a day in mid-December when they were shooting the home coverts near the house. My uncle, faced with mounting costs, had started to let three or four days' shooting during the season to an agency. The agency provided the guns, Uncle Cyril provided the shooting — as he saw fit! It was not an arrangement which had been going for very long. On this particular occasion — the last drive of the day, and, as the paying guns had been led to believe, the best — Blackall and his beaters went their way, Uncle Cyril and the guns went theirs.

'Clatworth Big Wood is, as the name suggests, a large conifer wood quartered by two broad rides at right angles to one another running the length of the covert. It provides two separate drives, but that day apparently there was only time for one before the light went. There were two lines of pegs which remained in position for the season, one line down one section of the wood, and the other beginning the further side of the intersecting ride; the numbers of course facing different directions and in reverse order. My uncle gave his guns a brief lecture on the need to keep quiet, led them to the first line of pegs with the numbers facing outward, despatched each to his allotted position, and blew his whistle sharply for the drive to begin. In the distance there was an answering whistle. The guns stood ready. The first few birds made their appearance, the right-hand gun had two or three shots, then pheasant after pheasant flew over the eight lonely sticks, each bearing just a small white card to mark its purpose, away to the right down the ride.

'When he is angry — which is quite often — Uncle Cyril has a habit of pacing around in a small circle like a dog about to pee. I can see him now gyrating in fury at the prospect of having to apologise for what appeared to be his mistake to guns he was apt to describe to his cronies as "Second-class season-ticket holders". The fact that their money kept his shoot going totally escaped his notice.

'The following day Blackall was summarily dismissed with a month's wages instead of notice. The gamekeeper took his case for wrongful dismissal to an industrial tribunal. At the hearing he stated that he had been specifically instructed by his master to beat out that end of Clatworth Big Wood; he went on to suggest the reason for this was because Lord St Helens did not want to have too many of his pheasants shot, and had given the instruction on purpose so that he could blame his keeper for what had gone wrong, and get rid of him at the same time.

'My uncle was represented at the hearing by a solicitor with a formidable reputation, known locally as Roaring Jack. He put it to the tribunal that such unsupported evidence, so defamatory to his noble client's character and reputation, was in itself grounds for a prosecution against the gamekeeper for slander. In the event of Lord St Helens being found guilty of wrongful dismissal, he would feel in duty bound to advise his client to bring such a prosecution.

'The members of the tribunal withdrew for consideration of the case. During the recess Roaring Jack buttonholed Blackall, who was unrepresented. The solicitor asked him whether it was his intention to seek further employment as a gamekeeper, and suggested if that was so he would need some kind of reference. He had been instructed by Lord St Helens to make what he considered to be a most generous offer, said Roaring Jack, a reasonable reference and £250 in cash in exchange for withdrawing the claim for wrongful dismissal. Naturally, added the solicitor, the offer was conditional on its remaining confidential.

'Blackall accepted, and when the tribunal reassembled he withdrew his claim without further explanation.

'The present gamekeeper at Clatworth comes from Sussex. It is his first season there.

'There is a strange counter-grain in the English character which will accept, even welcome, being insulted − by the right person. A cross word at work, an unkind remark from a friend, or a wife's below-the-belt insult, and we're up in arms. But go to a pub which boasts a "character" for a landlord, and he'll dish out broadsides of bad-taste humour at his customers' expense, and they'll come flocking back for more. At the upper-crust end of this phenomenon a lord can still get away with a lot. Uncle Cyril took this for granted. He didn't work at insulting people, it came naturally to him; yet his paying guests − guns − still came back for more.

'On one occasion, my uncle had let a day to the agency. He did not carry a gun himself − I believe he considered it beneath his dignity actually to shoot with his paying guests − but walked around with a long stick giving orders, to guns or beaters, it didn't matter which. Apart from the cash received, this was the one pleasure he got out of such days.

'It had become his custom to size up the guns when they arrived and decide from the look of them whom he would pick on. He would then carry out a preliminary verbal reconnaissance with a series of staccato questions, usually starting with "Pleased ter have yer here, what's yer name?" never mentioning his own, presuming the prospect knew it already. Having selected his victims he would stand behind one of them each drive, watch, comment, and end up casually poking at the spent cartridges with the end of his stick, before

24

turning his back on the unfortunate man and walking away without so much as another word.

'There was an occasion when my uncle was completely nonplussed by one of his "Second-class season-ticket holders".

'Waiting for the guns to arrive at the rendezvous on one of his let days, Uncle Cyril watched with interest as a young man got out of the sort of car which he called "too flashy by half". The young man was wearing a striped blazer and trousers. My uncle watched as this man substituted a Barbour coat for his blazer, pulled on a pair of green wellington boots, and then withdrew from a cricket bag in the boot of his car the barrels, fore-end, and stock of a shotgun. Having assembled the gun, he took out a cartridge bag, then a half bottle of whisky which he thrust into the pocket of his Barbour coat. Uncle Cyril watched these proceedings with interest and made a mental note to pay the young man a visit at his stand on the first available opportunity. Then he stumped off to marshal the guns.

'Off they went to the first stand, led by my uncle. After he had posted his guns, and blown his whistle for the drive to begin, he strode casually over to stand behind this young Philistine.

'The unbidden presence of my uncle behind one of his paying guest guns at the commencement of a drive usually provoked some sort of greeting, from them, not from him. If it did not, Uncle Cyril simply grunted his presence, and stood there leaning on his stick. This young man took absolutely no notice of him, did not even look round when he grunted. My uncle is not a man who takes kindly to being ignored.

'It was a windy day, and most of the birds flew forward to the end of the covert where the guns were standing then, faced with the prospect of a cross-wind flight in the open, allowed themselves to be swept away over the tops of the trees and back in a wide arc to the depths of the wood which they had just left. With the occasional exception they were very long shots indeed.

'As the drive progressed and more and more birds went the same way, the instincts of a lifetime shooting pheasants took precedence over Uncle Cyril's parsimony in seeing too many of his own being shot. So far he had contented himself with grunting, now his grunts became more and more intelligible until they were shaped into words, and words into shouts. "Shoot 'em, shoot 'em," he bellowed. "You don't come here not to shoot at my pheasants, shoot 'em."

'The young man in front of him took absolutely no notice; his gun remained tucked under his arm in the conventional resting position. Then a flush of birds broke further out into the open before beginning their downwind turn, up came the gun into his shoulder, a couple of reports, and two of them crumpled in flight and, propelled by the wind, dropped to the ground forty yards off. My uncle's young guest opened his gun to eject the spent cartridges, closed it again unloaded, picked up his cartridge bag from the ground, and turned to face his heckler. He dropped the cartridge bag at my uncle's feet, broke open the gun and proffered it to him. "Now you have a go yourself while I have a drink," he said.

'You will so far have gathered that my uncle does not subscribe to the view that the customer is always right. He regarded his shooting customers as a bunch of jumped-up tradesmen, and treated them accordingly. They for their part — or those of them that came back for more — regarded him as a bit of a character, and made allowances for what they presumably regarded as his aristocratic crankiness. Perversely, many did come back for more.

'One party of guns had been taking a couple of days each season at Clatworth for several years. The guns had been shooting together regularly and they had formed a roving syndicate; they didn't rent and organise a shoot of their own, but relied on the sporting agency to arrange for them a set number of days each season on various established shoots which would let casual days. It was an arrangement that suited them well: they could all shoot together, nobody had to organise anything, and they got variety. In addition to this they could all stay together in a hotel when this was necessary.

'One of the syndicate members was an estate agent from the West Midlands. On one occasion at Clatworth he brought a guest who was in the same line of business as himself. It happened that the estate agent and his guest were drawn at opposite ends of the line of guns, and so on one drive where two of the guns were required to walk with the beaters, these two found themselves the walking guns.

'Up until this moment the estate agent had not had a chance to see how his guest was getting on. Now was his opportunity to find out.

'Before the drive started, the keeper asked the estate agent's guest to walk down the ride in line with the beaters. Fifty yards further on, where the estate agent himself was asked to walk through the wood, there was no ride. The keeper told him there was a clearing right at the end, and when he reached that he should stop there because some of the birds would go back and he would get plenty of shooting. They heard a distant whistle and the drive began.

'The estate agent had to pick his way through the trees, but he could hear his guest banging merrily away to the right of him and edged himself over in that direction, slipping down the line from beater to beater, until he could see the clearing.

'By contrast the estate agent's guest was having a fine time, the going was easy and there was plenty to shoot as the pheasants got up and made their way forward. There was no one with whom he had to share his sport, the beaters were busy in the dense wood on either side; he was alone there on the open ride to enjoy himself. Once or twice he thought he heard shouts from the end of the wood, but he didn't take any notice and strode on down the ride pausing only to fire and reload.

'Half way through the wood now, the estate agent's guest heard the popping of guns ahead; now he definitely heard someone shouting. If they wanted to shout that was their affair, he didn't take any notice, and continued on his way loosing off whenever a bird got up within sixty yards of him.

27

The shouts continued, he noticed, whenever he shot. He could make out the words now – or some of them – it sounded like, "Let 'em come forward blarst yer"; the rest was indistinguishable. What, and let you have all the shooting, he thought to himself, not bloody likely! A nice low bird got up and made its way straight down the ride. The estate agent's guest gave it both barrels. This produced a positive volley of shouts. There was no mistaking the abusive content of them now. Whoever it was at the end of that wood certainly had it in for him for some reason or another.

'In his business career the estate agent's guest had rapidly learnt the dangers of direct confrontation – it had become second nature to him to avoid it whenever he could – so now he set his mind to avoiding a confrontation with the angry man at the end of the wood. It wasn't a very difficult problem initially, simply hang about in the wood until the shooting – and the shouting – was over. He let the beaters go on ahead of him and took to the undergrowth.

'The drive was well under way before Uncle Cyril saw what was happening: this damned grocer shooting at the pheasants coming forward, and shooting bloody low. He shouted at the man, who took no notice. My uncle ducked as a blast of shot rattled against the leaves of a holly bush behind him. There was only one answer: to go after the man.

'By now the estate agent had reached the clearing at the end of the covert where he had been told by the keeper to stand and wait for birds breaking back. After struggling through the undergrowth, he was looking forward to a bit of shooting at last.

'Uncle Cyril emerged from cover onto the main ride and looked around him for the offending gun. No sign of anyone. His quarry, the estate agent's guest, was also breaking cover – on his way home. There were two shots close by. Uncle Cyril moved in.

'He saw the estate agent, and launched his attack. "I saw yer, yer dangerous blackguard, not content with maulin' me pheasants, yer do yer best to cut me down as well. Go home damn yer, go home." The voice, pitched at full volume from a few yards behind, nearly made the unfortunate man drop his gun. He swung round in utter surprise to be confronted by my uncle's contorted face. That alone must have been enough to shake the estate agent's morale; the abuse that followed convinced him that there was no point in reasoning with this raving despot. He went, without bothering to enquire further about his guest.

'My Uncle Cyril, still trembling with wrath but with only a retreating back upon which to vent it, went in search of his keeper to curse him roundly for failing to supervise the walking guns properly.

'Some three or four times each year it was my Uncle Cyril's custom to go up to London. These visits were usually made to coincide with a debate in the House of Lords which interested him, agricultural subsidies or the return of capital punishment, something like that. My uncle could kill a number of birds with one stone: make his feelings known during the debate by grunting, muttering or fidgeting, meet some of his cronies, return to his club and dine there; then go out leaving a message with the porter to provide him with an alibi in case my Aunt Isobel telephoned. All of this subsidised by collecting his travelling and attendance allowance from the Lords.

'A week or so before each visit, Uncle Cyril would summon the current gamekeeper and order him to prepare for the journey. This involved the man in sprucing up the Austin Princess, which had been bought at the end of the war as a substitute for the ailing Daimler, brushing and pressing the chauffeur's uniform which had been handed on to him, and arriving suitably dressed at the front door of Clatworth House an hour before the train was due to depart.

'Incidentally, Blackall notched up the first penalty point during his time in my uncle's employment by refusing to undertake this extra-curricular duty. He said that if he'd wanted to be a chauffeur he would have applied for the job, but as a gamekeeper he had no intention of dressing up in a

29

motor cycle policeman's uniform which did not fit, with a flat hat on his head.

'The drive from Clatworth to the nearest main-line railway station took twenty-five minutes. Uncle Cyril allowed an hour for the journey. The unexpended portion of the travelling time was spent sitting in the back of the car parked in front of the station booking hall reading *The Times*, and occasionally pulling out his watch and looking at the time. Then, if all went well with British Rail, he would board the train for London.

'It was in February of the year following the events I have already told you about that my Uncle Cyril appointed to go to London on one of his regular visits. It seemed as good a time as any to go, the weather at home was cold, the shooting season had finished, and he noticed that the House of Lords would be considering Amendments to the Night Poaching Act, 1828.

'The middle of the afternoon, and their lordships were endeavouring to decide whether a crossbow should be defined as an "engine or other instrument". At that point in the debate my uncle fell asleep.

'"And what, my lords, would you do in the same circumstances?" The speaker appealed to the feelings of his noble colleagues at the culmination of a speech he had been working on for weeks. These challenging words seemed to penetrate my uncle's subconscious meanderings. He came to with a start. "Hang the beggars, no point in wasting taxpayers' money keeping 'em in jail, hang the beggars," he growled thickly.

'"Bit stiff for a trespasser in pursuit of game who refuses to give his name and address, isn't it?" said a voice from the bench alongside him.

'My uncle looked round. He saw a young man with a vaguely familiar face. Uncertain whether or not he was having his leg pulled, my uncle resorted to his usual tactic based on the theory that attack is the best form of defence. First he fixed his interlocutor with a basilisk stare to soften him up, then ignoring the import of his words, chose his own thrust. "Didn't notice yer before," he hissed in a stage whisper, "D'you come here often?"

'"My first visit," said the young man unabashed, "I thought if I came to sit near you, Lord St Helens, I'd be bound to pick up a few tips, like I did last time we met. Don't you remember, out shooting, you came over to give me the benefit of your experience? Unfortunately I haven't got any whisky with me today." '

Chapter Four

Hawk Bells Ring the Changes

Sam Rashleigh was a stirrer. He would edge his way into the conversation, pretend to listen attentively for a while, then make some remark or ask a direct question which he thought would ginger things up; it usually did, but not always the way Sam intended. I do not think he meant to be tiresome; he was a good-natured person, but he simply could not resist the urge to provoke.

On the occasion I am writing about now, I heard Sam from the other side of the dinner table, at his usual conversational gambit of poking the fire to see if he could make the sparks fly.

'Remember Bernie Cornfeld and his Pyramid Selling?' he asked, addressing the question to no one in particular. We did not, but Sam continued. 'He was the con-man in the Sixties who came up with the slogan, "Do you seriously want to be rich?" '

A pause while Sam glanced around to see if this spark had ignited any interest, and on he went. 'I never did understand what Pyramid Selling was all about, but you have to admit that slogan was a clever one, it implied that anyone could be really rich, if only they took the trouble to find out how. Just contact Bernie Cornfeld of course! It's one thing seriously wanting to be rich, but I wonder how many people think beyond that to the next stage, what they want to do when they are rich. Just supposing you became seriously rich, what would you do? You all enjoy your shooting, so presumably you would spend some of your new-found wealth on that. But how?'

'I know what I'd do,' said Billy Clavering without hesitation, 'I'd take a really good shoot in Hampshire, not far away from my father-in-law who reckons he's got one of the best partridge shoots in England, then I'd arrange all my shooting days except one to coincide with his. And I wouldn't ask him that day.'

Ask a silly question! And it was a silly question for Sam Rashleigh to ask. Apart from anything else, he was in as good a position as any to answer it himself. As a prosperous merchant banker, earning a salary only to be guessed at after reading the City pages of the newspapers, he of all of us would seem to have the least need to take advantage of any sudden access of wealth.

Someone said, 'That's an interesting question, Sam. How did you manage to cope with the problem?'

Sam did not appreciate having the tables turned on him, and made a determined attempt to disengage. 'I'm not in the seriously rich bracket,' he declared, 'I just earn a decent salary...'

'Not to mention share options, productivity bonuses, expenses, and other related fringe benefits, as I think you City people euphemistically call them. And I don't suppose you ever offer any of your clients a day's shooting! Or does that come out of your entertainment allowance? If I were in your shoes, Sam, I'd take the extra cash and spend it on a damn great yacht you can cruise off to the Bahamas in when the shooting season is over.'

Most of us knew that the speaker, John Dishforth, had taken a bad knock as a name at Lloyd's. It was even possible that he would have to sell the family estate in Lincolnshire to cover his losses.

But John did not leave it at that. 'It's all very well when you can buy your shooting by the bird, if that's what you want. Like ordering dinner: choose from the menu, pay the bill and go home. You try turning two thousand acres and a crumbling mansion into a going concern. Then when you've put the lot in hock to keep it going, the clever City guys close in and say you've got to sell up to pay your gambling debts. Go looking for your shooting in ten years time, Sam, and you won't find any, or if you do you'll find it a bit different. Why? Because damn fools like me will have pulled out of the country estate business to realise the asset value. The professionals will have taken over where our grandfathers left off.'

Let emotion loose amongst a group of Englishmen dining together, and the result is an uncomfortable silence around the table. It was broken by Simon Barrington.

'Perhaps we shouldn't get too personal about Sam's hypothetical question,' said he soothingly. 'Some of our grandfathers didn't spend money on shooting, they spent fortunes. And lost them too. You might be interested in the story of one estate which must have swallowed up more money on shooting than most.'

That is how I recall the conversation which led up to Simon Barrington's tale. Although fresh in my mind, I could hardly have recorded it verbatim; it is freely translated from memory. And at this point I think I had better leave the dialogue, and tell you Simon's tale free of any of the interruptions you might expect from two dozen or so people sitting around a dinner table.

'Drive along the main Norwich to London road, the A11; just as you are about to leave Norfolk and enter Suffolk, the road signs will direct you to the market town of Thetford. You carry on along the bypass. You are in Breckland. Breckland consists of areas of forestry, and open spaces of light sandy soil interspersed with shelter-belts. You are travelling south. Three miles on, the universal conifers to the east of the road give way to a wider variety of trees. If you glance out of the nearside window of your car through the trees you will see a sweep of parkland and catch a glimpse of a big mansion. Lodges and estate cottages indicate that you are passing through a large estate. The sign beside the road says Elveden. A mile further and on the right you will see a fluted stone column of similar size to the one in Trafalgar

34

Square, only Nelson is missing from the top. You wonder who or what it commemorates. Then you come to the wire perimeter fence of the US Air Base at Lakenheath.

'The column is surely one of the biggest war memorials in rural England, and carved in the stone above you will see the names of Viscount Elveden and a handful of estate workers who lost their lives in the service of their country during the Second World War. Lord Elveden, only son of brewer and philanthropist Edward Cecil Guinness, second Earl of Iveagh, was killed in Holland the year the war ended.

'In 1894 the first Earl, Ernest Guinness, bought the twenty-five-thousand-acre Elveden Estate and the mansion you have just passed. The estate had been one of the most important shoots in the country, and Lord Iveagh set about restoring it to that position. In the days before crop-growing techniques were properly developed, the light sandy heathland was little good for agriculture, but very good for game. The shooting was under the management of a Game Department with a staff of seventy men, and produced over a hundred thousand head a year, a hundred and forty-five thousand in the best year at the beginning of the 1920s.

'The biggest one-day bag at Elveden was made on Guy Fawkes Day 1912, when five guns, including King George V, killed nearly three thousand two hundred and fifty head of game. A supporting cast of over a hundred, including keepers, under-keepers, pickers-up, beaters, loaders, cartridge boys, not to mention domestic staff, served the five guns. Next day the bag was a bit smaller, only two and a half thousand head. The King gave up in the afternoon because his shoulder was too painful. But he was back again the following day, when again they topped the two thousand mark. The total for three days' sport, not far short of eight thousand head!

'When the King of England shot at Elveden, which three did, everything was planned for that day well before the beginning of the season. Special game-holding crops were planted in the spring, hand-reared birds were put down in the beats they were going to shoot over when the King came, and all the earlier shoots were kept well away from the Royal preserve. Everyone on the estate was fully briefed before the great day came, and nothing — except presumably the weather — was left to chance. There were usually five guns including His Majesty, and the King's stand each drive – in the best place, of course – was indicated by a stick with the bark peeled off.

'In 1927 the first Earl died. The new Earl of Iveagh was granted an audience with the King to hand over his father's Insignia of the Thistle. The King is reported to have said to him, "I trust you are going to keep up the shooting at Elveden, I shall hope to come next year, and I think the Queen would like to come, too." It was generally considered to be the death of the King nine years later, rather than that of his father, which freed the second Earl of his obligation to run Elveden as one vast shoot and allowed him to develop the agricultural potential of the estate.

'In the next decade the bags at Elveden dropped, but the estate still provided an average of seventy-five-thousand head a year right up to the outbreak of the war, and even during the war the average was twenty-five-thousand a year. Firstly British troops took over the estate as a training area, then Elveden became the Headquarters of the Eighth United States Air Force. For the American airmen stationed there, shooting game, which Lord Iveagh allowed them to do over part of the estate, must have been one of the more unusual perks enjoyed by servicemen anywhere.

'During the war I lived nearby, and actually shot there once, a memorable day for a boy of sixteen. I went with my stepfather who had been asked by Captain William Bunbury who ran the shooting for Lord Iveagh; even in wartime – just a small day by Elveden standards, cocks only – we shot a hundred and thirty-seven.

'Captain Bunbury himself was sufficiently awe-inspiring as a host, for he looked as if he had stepped straight out of a Spy cartoon, but Turner the head keeper was even more formidable, or at least in my imagination he was. Here was this stocky figure wearing the old-fashioned keeper's undress uniform of broad-brimmed felt hat, full-skirted coat, shooting breeches and gaiters, who in his time had touched his full-dress bowler to kings, the upper crust of society, and all the best shots in the country. And here was I trying to look as if I belonged, and could shoot straight. I remember, too, the curious brass horn Turner (how should I address him if he spoke to me?) carried slung over his shoulder. The instrument looked like a sort of quadripartite hunting horn with a valve in the middle; later I heard its unmelodious calls signalling to the beaters to do his bidding. I wonder where that horn is now; I never saw its like again.

'I looked that day up in the scappy gamebook I started to keep and never kept up: there is the date, the ninth of January 1942. At least I can say that I have shot at Elveden. People pay good money these days to be able to say that. But to continue the story of the estate. There is another memorial of note in Elveden which you do not see from the road. You have to look for it in the undistinguished church which stands in the park. The tomb which you will find there bears the inscription, "Duleep Singh, Maharajah of Lahore, GCSI. Born in the Punjab 4th September 1838. Died in Paris 22nd October 1893." A more imposing memorial to the first squire of Elveden stands a few hundred yards away, the Hall itself. The central feature of this architectural extravaganza, designed to make an Eastern prince feel at home in a foreign land, is a huge marble chamber surmounted by a copper dome which can be seen above the trees for miles around. It is reputedly the coldest room in Europe.

'Duleep Singh, Maharajah of Lahore, had a difficult childhood. His father, Runjit Singh, Ruler of the Punjab, acknowledged him as his son. Paternity by decree! It was a convenient adoption procedure for a despot who made the law to suit the circumstance. The circumstances were that Runjit Singh had been through two strokes, was partially paralysed, and much preferred the company of pretty boys to that of his wife, the Rani Jindan. It was politically expedient for the wily old Lion of the Punjab to proclaim his fatherhood, and get the credit from the gullible mass of his subjects for his continued virility. It also further secured his dynasty, although Duleep was the Rani's fourth son!

'The Rani Jindan was reputed to be the daughter of a palace doorkeeper favoured by the Maharajah. She was a woman of considerable wit, personality, staying power, and lack of sexual inhibition. It was said that her husband took a vicarious pleasure in watching her amorous antics with his current favourite, formerly one of the palace water-carriers. The old "Lion" Runjit Singh died before his acknowledged offspring was a year old.

'By the time he was six, most of young Duleep's other relations had either died or been murdered; he actually witnessed his uncle being bayoneted to death. Meanwhile his mother intrigued, plotted, and seduced her way to seeing her youngest son on the throne of the Punjab. In this she succeeded, and he was proclaimed Maharajah of Lahore, the Rani, with her current lover in attendance, acting as Regent. The deteriorating situation amongst the rebellious Sikhs, with the Rani at the centre of it, was one that the British Raj could no longer tolerate. The Treaty of Lahore finally put an end to Duleep Singh's future as Ruler of the Punjab.

'Duleep Singh was taken from the custody of his mother, removed from the Punjab and put in the charge of a Scottish tutor.

'The deposed Maharajah first came to England at the age of sixteen, by which time he had been a ward of the British Government since he was twelve. Any doubts that might have been expressed about the vintage of the royal blood in Duleep's veins were dispelled by Queen Victoria, who declared unequivocally that he had been acknowledged as Runjit Singh's son, "And placed on the throne by Lord Hardinge". He was accorded the rank, title, and privileges of a European prince.

'As a boy Duleep was a great favourite of Queen Victoria's.

When he first came to lunch with the Queen, she wrote in her journal, "He was beautifully dressed and covered with diamonds. The Koh-i-noor belonged to, and was once worn by him. I always feel so much for these poor deposed Indian princes."

'The Queen also noted with satisfaction that Duleep Singh was now a Christian, having been baptised the previous year.

'In 1863, at the age of twenty-five, Duleep Singh bought the seventeen thousand acre Elveden estate for £105,000 raised on a 4 per cent loan from the India Office, reputedly having first turned down Sandringham the previous year.

'I have often wondered how an exiled Indian prince came by his taste for shooting English pheasants and partridges. His experience of sport in India must have been very different. There are pictures of him as a boy out hunting, but the hunting was done with hawk and hound. The fact is that within thirty years Duleep Singh had turned an insignificant Suffolk estate into one of the finest sporting properties in England, to rank with the other great shoots concentrated in the northern half of East Anglia: Euston, Merton, Quidenham, Holkham, Thornham, and Sandringham.

'With his connections amongst the English aristocracy, I suppose it was natural that Duleep should discover the delights of shooting driven game, recently made possible by the invention of the percussion-fired breech-loading shotgun. All the names associated with shooting on the grand scale in the latter part of the nineteenth century were guests of the Maharajah's at Elveden: the Prince of Wales, Lords Ripon and Walsingham, the two best shots in England, and runners-up too numerous to mention from the top slice of society. The Maharajah himself, portly by this time, was considered to be one of the half dozen best shots in the country; quick but inelegant, spinning on his feet like a teetotum to seize the second gun from his loader.

'Duleep also had a penchant for shooting rabbits; the light sandy soil at Elveden teemed with them. He had wooden platforms erected in suitable places, and the rabbits in their hundreds were driven towards him standing there on one of these platforms. Maybe it reminded him of shooting more dangerous game in India, or perhaps it was just a practical notion to give him a better field of fire. Who knows? But all the tenants on the estate got a couple of rabbits each at Christmas.

'In addition to the shooting at Elveden, Duleep Singh rented grouse moors in Yorkshire and Scotland, and made frequent sporting tours to the Danube. He claimed two records: seven hundred and eighty partridges to his own gun for the expenditure of a thousand cartridges at Elveden; and four hundred and forty grouse shot by himself in a day at Grandtully, the place he rented in Perthshire. On the record grouse day, he had three pairs of dogs working the hill for him; as soon as he had finished shooting over one pair of pointing dogs, he was up on his pony and off to the next point. He began shooting at five in the morning, and finished in the late afternoon.

'By now the money was beginning to run out. The trouble was that the Maharajah was not seriously rich, not by the standards of his friends and contemporaries. He took the view that the allowance he got from the India Office was quite inadequate to maintain the way of life to which he considered himself entitled. The India Office took exactly the opposite view. Expenditure mounted inexorably over income. Attempts to extract more money from the Government, usually channelled through Queen Victoria, met with sympathy from her (her Crown Jewels, after all, contained the Koh-i-noor diamond, once the property of Duleep's father), but with indifference from the India Office.

'Whatever his financial problems, Duleep did not let them interfere too much with his shooting. By 1885 things were beginning to look desperate, and he was forced to consider putting Elveden up for auction. But when the season opened in the autumn, once again there was a big shooting party at Elveden with the bag in the thousands, and the Maharajah once again the genial host.

'Over the next few years Duleep Singh progressively turned his back on England, embittered by his lack of success in getting what he considered to be his rightful inheritance. He renounced Christianity, and travelled in India and Russia trying to stir up Sikh nationalism on the North-West Frontier.

'From Russia he wrote to his son Victor to say how happy he was in that country, where there was plenty of grouse shooting and salmon fishing in the north, woodcock shooting on the Black Sea coast, snipe and wildfowl in the Crimea. "If not better employed," he wrote, "he meant to indulge himself in some first-class sport".

'He kept up a one-way correspondence with Queen Victoria, mostly complaining about being swindled out of his kingdom by her Christian Government, and ending, "The deeply wronged legitimate Sovereign of the Sikhs, Duleep Singh, Maharajah".

'Meanwhile, the Elveden Estate had more or less been left to look after itself under the management of trustees appointed by the Government. The contents of the Hall had been sold off. The Duke of Grafton, Duleep's neighbour and loyal friend, described the situation on the estate: "16,000 acres without a labourer employed except under-keepers who are a disgrace to the place, also men temporarily employed without homes and living where they can."

'By now Duleep Singh was living in Paris. Towards the end of his life he recanted, wishing especially to become reconciled with Queen Victoria, for whom he always felt a special regard despite having labelled her "Mrs Fagin" over the expropriation of the Koh-i-noor diamond. He sought the Queen's forgiveness, which was granted.

'At the beginning of the pheasant shooting season of 1893, Duleep Singh, Maharajah of Lahore, one-time Squire of Elveden, died in Paris. His wife was away, the first time she had left him in the past two years, but his two young daughters used to come and see him every day. Among their favourite playthings were the silver hawk bells he had kept since boyhood, which he gave them on their last visit.

'The last occupants of Elveden Hall moved out at the end of the war, American servicemen of the US Air Force. The Guinnesses never lived there again. The third Earl of Iveagh was a shy man who had problems of his own, not the least of them Ernest Saunders. He developed an increasing preference for living on his property in Ireland. In 1984, almost exactly one hundred years after Duleep Singh put his furniture up for sale, the contents of the Hall were sold off by Christie's. Elveden Hall stands empty. The shooting? Well, they have kept up the shooting at Elveden, but I doubt if King George V would have approved!

'Forty years after I shot there, I went back to Elveden. I was there to see the headkeeper about some photographs for an article which I was writing. He showed them to me, faded and yellow in their heavy frames, taking them down off the walls of the room near the huge game larder which served him for an office. One photograph was of a shooting party before the Kaiser's War, not as usual just the guns but the complete ménage: keepers in their livery, loaders, beaters in their hard hats and smocks, and pickers-up, all of them formed up in two ranks occupying the entire breadth of the photograph. We talked about this and that, and it struck me how much a keeper of the old school has had to adapt to a new generation of guns. He told me with obvious pride that he had been loading for Captain Bunbury on his last day's shooting at Elveden. He told me of the American serviceman who had shot his first pheasant on the estate, shouting joyously after this feat, "I got me a rooster, I got me a rooster". And he told me about some of the guns who shoot at Elveden now. Conscious that I was taking up more than my fair share of his time, I thanked the keeper and said goodbye.

'I got into my car and drove away from the lodge. By this time it was past two o'clock, and I had not yet eaten my sandwiches. I was tempted by the idea of eating them in the park, but I thought I would feel a bit of a fool if anyone asked me what I was doing there munching away like a pushy tourist trying his luck. I did not suppose, though, that anyone would mind if I drove round the front of the house on my way out to the main road. I did so, parking alone on the wide gravel sweep; no one else in sight, just me and that great empty house which nobody wanted.

'I looked across to the church and wondered how many of the present-day parishioners who bring their children to be baptised, come there to marry, worship and be buried, know anything of Duleep Singh, Maharajah of Lahore. Why should they? At least they will not be in the same position as a previous generation of parishioners, of whom the rector of the time wrote: "The able-bodied portion in the parish will be compelled to seek for employment elsewhere — but what will come of the afflicted, the aged and the extremely poor I know not — for the schools, clubs, and charities, hitherto entirely supported by His Highness, will be supported by him no longer. The heart has gone out of the place."

'I started up the car, and drove off down the drive. As I passed a covert of tall fir trees, I stopped the car for a moment again, to wonder where they might have put the King's stand, marked by the stick with the bark peeled off. And I remembered the last tale which the headkeeper had told me half an hour earlier.

'A syndicate of Greek businessmen had taken a day's shooting at Elveden; one of them arrived with his two guns, a five-shot automatic and a double-barrelled sidelock, some firepower even if it is not the conventional two-gun combination. He fired a great many cartridges without much noticeable result. Towards the end of one drive a golden pheasant was forced into the open, flying low and slow as golden pheasants do if they fly at all, heading straight for the heavily armed Greek. The golden pheasant flew into a hail of shot and fell to the ground quite dead. Immediately the Greek sportsman dropped the gun in use and made a bee-line for the fallen pheasant. He grabbed the bird, bore it aloft, then did a lap of honour down the line of guns, shouting in triumph, *"Faisan royale, faisan royale"*.'

Chapter Five

Sinclair's Shoot

Boyhood memories can be a bore. How often have I read of some lad shooting his first pheasant; the setting, the ecstasy of the occasion, the pride with which the copper-coloured beauty (why is it never a hen?) is borne home in triumph, the congratulations and the contentment. But two boyhood memories of my own have stuck with me as an antidote to days when I have shot badly, days when I have been overawed by the company of the other guns, days when there has not been much to shoot, and days when I have had other things on my mind. They also have a bearing on the story which follows.

Picture first a lad of sixteen, asked to shoot in the final year of Hitler's war, with a party of fen farmers in that expanse of black flat land in the north of Cambridgeshire. Bedford Level it is called, and level it is, as far as the eye can see. The line of the horizon to the north is broken only by the blip of Ely Cathedral's pinnacles; to the south the black fen gives way to heath land in the direction of Newmarket, all around stretch acres of sugar beet and celery, a landscape of green and black without a covert to be seen. But the sugar beet and celery hold a plentiful stock of wild pheasants, and partridges too.

There are about twenty-five of us, some guns stand and some walk, the line of walkers thickened up with a dozen or so casual beaters; there is no keeper to direct operations, for the farmer whose land we are on does that. We do not draw for places because there are no pegs. The guns, those who are not walking, line out behind the bank of a convenient dyke. They know where to go, most of them have been beating and shooting here since boyhood. There is a good deal of banter.

It is the last drive of the short afternoon, and the sixteen-year-old lad is detailed off to stand. The drive begins. He can see the moving black dots of beaters in the sea of green half a mile away. There is an occasional bang, then faraway shouts of 'Forward'. The lad sees the pheasant, just one pheasant, gaining height all the way as it flies towards the dyke where the guns are standing. There is not another bird in the sky. It is still a couple of hundred yards away when someone further down the line shouts, 'Ten to one on the pheasant'. The lad realises that this is his pheasant, no one else could justifiably shoot at it. He ups with his gun, bang – once, and down comes the pheasant from forty yards up. There is a cheer down the line. I have never forgotten the occasion.

That memory is like a video recording, close my eyes and I can see it at will, hear the shout, 'Ten to one on the pheasant'. The other is far less dramatic, more a voice speaking to me from the past, but equally durable, and perhaps of greater significance in shaping the way I have looked for enjoyment from my shooting.

At roughly the same period in my life, I am walking around the hedgerows on an estate not twenty miles to the south of the green and black prairie of fenland; the land is light and sandy, there are belts and coverts which have been planted with shooting in mind, farmworkers' cottages nestle neatly into the landscape; it is a prospect of well-cared-for countryside, woodland, plough, roots, and tidy hedgerows. I am alone with an oldish man, the owner of the estate.

During the afternoon we have walked together with our guns, he and I, on either side of hedge or ditch, through any strip of cover likely to tempt a pheasant to occupy it as a preliminary to wandering further afield in search of grubs or grain. The third member of the party is a fat spaniel called Bones who snuffles noisily ahead of us, and turns to look at me with baleful eyes when I miss the bird which he has

45

managed to flush. When a bird gets up, I usually seem to be the one to shoot first; my host still has his gun tucked under his arm as I look in his direction after the success or failure of my shot.

In this manner we collect sufficient to make our game bags heavy (incidentally, does anyone teach young shooters these days to fold a shot bird's head under its wing before putting it in the bag?); the November afternoon threatens us with a failing light. It is time to turn for home. We retrace our steps towards the park and the rather ugly Victorian house at the end of the drive. My host quietly observes, 'Harry, remember this. There are no bad days' shooting, some days are just better than others'.

If I had been asked when I got home that same evening what we talked about, one generation and the next, in between the serious business of hunting hedgerow pheasants, I would not have been able to say. Only that I had tried to be polite, ingratiating maybe, in the hope of being asked to shoot again. My host's conversation utterly eludes me, except for that one remark.

It is a pity many people today fail to appreciate that field sports have more to do with simple pleasure than social credibility. And Desmond Grattan's story might serve to remind those who take their shooting too seriously of this basic fact.

'I have a farm,' Desmond told us, 'which is too small to make into a shoot proper, but there is enough wild game about to make it worthwhile inviting a few friends to see what we can pick up in a morning, walking around with the occasional improvised drive. A week or two before Christmas some years ago I thought it would be fun to have a Boxing Day shoot, so I telephoned a friend who lives nearby and has a few more acres to throw into the pot, suggesting we pool our resources to make a day of it, taking into account a longish lunch.

'It so happened that this friend, Henry Sinclair his name is, had achieved an ambition by getting his three brothers, plus wives and assorted children, to stay over Christmas. My impromptu shoot took on a fresh dimension.

'It was agreed between Henry and me that we would shoot over my farm during the morning, have a late lunch at his house, then a final drive out of the one sizeable wood there. This Henry said would be the drive of the day; he had been working on it to attract any pheasants which strayed too far away from a big syndicate shoot nearby.

'We met, the usual gathering for such an occasion, fifteen or so in all, half of the party carrying guns; the other half, wives, daughters, children old enough to walk, the beaters. A variety of dogs accompanying the party greeted each other with varying degrees of suspicion, aggression, or sexual interest.

'I did not know Henry's brothers, but as I knew practically everyone else, it was not difficult to identify them before being introduced. I guessed the Sinclair brothers had had a merrier Christmas than most, not difficult on the evidence of their appearance and conversation; I further suspected that one of them − the youngest − had freshened up the residual alcohol in his system at some stage since breakfast. This band of brothers formed a party within a party; their obvious pleasure of being together once again rubbed off on the rest of us and made them very good company indeed. The prospects for the day ahead, whatever there was to shoot, looked anything but dull.

'It soon struck me that a keen sense of rivalry existed amongst the Sinclair brothers. The moment a bird took wing they shot at it, all of them. The challenge seemed to be which of them could let his gun off first.

'For an hour or so we marched and counter-marched over what looked like promising pheasant territory, the line a little ragged in places as the morning wore on. Nothing escaped being shot at, but very little was actually shot. Then we came to the place which I had been reserving as the main counter-attraction to Henry's much vaunted home covert in the afternoon, a strip of rough grass and rushes where I was pretty sure there had to be some birds. We paused to regroup.

'We lined out for this final battue before lunch. I gave the signal to advance.

'There were a lot more pheasants in that strip of rushy wasteland than I thought there would be, and they held their ground resolutely in the face of skirmishing dogs and advancing line of noisy guns. When forced to take to the wing the birds that met their death met it with certainty; once safely airborne others made their escape whilst their assailants were reloading. It was the initial volley which took its toll. If a bird survived that, it could expect to roost in peace for the night. The unluckiest pheasant of all, an old cock who knew what he was about, sat it out until we were nearly on top of him, then, nosed out by one of the dogs, got up and flew through the hail of shot which greeted his appearance, gaining height to make good the escape which he would have much preferred to have done on foot.

'Then the cock pheasant swung back, relying on altitude to keep him out of trouble, to make for the big wood to the rear of us. His flight path would take him within range of our right flank, if he held his course. From my position on the higher ground over on the left flank I saw the line of guns and attendant family beaters strung out across the little valley, waiting and watching the approaching cock pheasant. The bird flew straight and high, disregarding any danger below, knowing exactly where he intended to get to; he had heard the bang of many a gun before, I guessed, and was wary enough to take evasive action if he thought it necessary. His line of flight was deliberate, he was contemptuous of our efforts to bring him down.

'Even a day like this, happy-go-lucky and relaxed, no one taking any notice of who shoots well or who shoots badly, can have its moments of suspense. Here was this one bird that had chosen to show us how a pheasant can fly. I knew that someone must shoot soon. I did not register who it was likely to be because I did not think he would have any success. I fully expected to hear the sound of the shots, and see the continued thrust of wing-beat until the outline of the pheasant was eclipsed by the dark trees of the wood.

'Then the unexpected happened, the old cock pheasant folded in flight and fell; simultaneously I heard a single report from the other side of the valley. It was not until I heard the chorus of approval that I realised who had fired the shot. It was my sixteen-year-old son Charlie.

'After lunch we meandered around some muddy fields to shake down our meal and whet our appetites for the big drive which was to follow. I noticed one of the Sinclair brothers, the one who looked as if he might have been topping up a bit that morning, had brought a bottle with him this time. He was, as the Irish say, "Not drunk, but having drink taken". Since he seemed intent on going his own way, which was not in the same direction as the rest of us, and was in the care of an attractive young lady, we left him to his own devices. I collected the other guns, and Henry Sinclair assembled the beaters for the final drive of the day.

'In position at the end of the long wood which runs the length of Henry's property, we waited for the first pheasants to make their appearance. We could as yet hear nothing of the beaters except the faint yapping of a dog well ahead of them in the covert. Well, I thought to myself, it's a long wood and there aren't any back guns to deal with birds going the wrong way, you wouldn't expect to hear any shooting so soon.

'We continued to wait, distant voices and the occasional clang of a stick on metal could be heard from the covert in front of us. But still no pheasants. Then I heard a couple of shots from the direction of the house, wondered for a moment who could be there, and thought no more about it. I was beginning to have my doubts, though, about the outcome of the big drive. Henry would surely be expecting to hear shots by this time. I could imagine his disappointment if this much vaunted drive turned out to be a flop. It had been a nice morning followed by a very good lunch provided by Henry's wife; if there was nothing more for us to shoot we could at least keep Henry happy a little longer by pretending that there was. I did a hasty tour of the other guns, a word of explanation sufficed, and we all began banging away at imaginary pheasants.

'The motley of beaters were now half way through the wood, and we could hear their shrill voices with Henry's tenor solo of Hi-hi-his and Ho-ho-hos dominating the discord. He must have thought the birds were very wild when the shooting began, because he could not have seen any evidence of pheasant activity himself, but the continued banging of the guns ahead must have served its purpose and raised his expectations; his instructions to keep in line and to go steady took on fresh urgency.

'Apart from the spasmodic appearances of a busy terrier hunting something interesting, the first sign that the drive was over was the emergence from the wood of a small boy, carrying a stick nearly the same size as himself, in floods of tears; his mother followed uttering words of comfort. We had stopped firing by then, having wasted enough of our cartridges for Henry's benefit. The other beaters straggled out of the wood, picking up their bearings, waiting for further instructions. Henry Sinclair strode purposefully forward. "Well, how did you chaps get on, I heard plenty of shooting," he said. We were prepared for this: very high birds we told him, overdid it a bit at lunch, couldn't touch a feather, and any other excuse that came readily to mind.

'What had actually happened did not immediately occur to Henry. At that moment there was a shout from the direction of the house and we looked round to see the Sinclair brother, the one with the bottle, approaching us with his lady friend in tow. "What a useless lot you are," he said, "at least I bloody well managed to shoot something." He held up a mallard drake. The only duck I had seen that afternoon had been quacking contentedly on the moat round the house.'

Chapter Six

Parson Radford

'When I was at school,' said Humphrey Chance, 'there was a chap in the same form called Lang. He had a great big nose and was immediately christened Beaky Lang. One day he held his hand up in class and asked to be excused. Well, you know the schoolboy code, score points off the form master if you can, but don't lose face. Standing up in front of everyone and asking permission to go and have a pee is definitely losing face. He was immediately rechristened Leaky Bang.'

'Knowing the rules of the game, you could say the lad asked for it,' said someone. 'The boys I feel sorry for are the ones who start with the disadvantage of having an unfortunate name. We had a chap when I was at school name of Brain, initial P'.

'And that,' said David Radford, 'puts me in mind of one Robin Sherston Hole who I was at school with, and who is still one of my greatest friends. School name-tapes with R. S. Hole embroidered on them are rather eyecatching, as Robin Hole's mother must have discovered when she sewed them on. Robin Hole began life with this handicap because his mother's maiden name had been Sherston. She had a sister but no brothers; when she married Matthew Hole and their first child was born, a son, she was determined that the family name should be preserved. He was christened Robin Sherston Hole.

'The unfortunate juxtaposition of Robin's initials leapt from the notice-board in the school hall where I and several other boys were studying the list of new boys at the beginning of term. What a cross for a thirteen-year-old to bear; what a bonanza for his contemporaries!

'It says a great deal for Robin that he overcame this parentally imposed handicap by an easy charm, plenty of self-confidence, and in the last resort a bruising right hook that quickly got him into the school boxing team. With such attributes it was unwise to take liberties with Robin Hole.

'I made friends at school because on the whole it was a great deal easier to make friends than it was to make enemies. I lost most of these school friends later on in life, lost them in the sense that they went their way and I went mine, too many things happening at the age of eighteen to keep in touch. I was not concerned with the lasting quality of friendship then, only with the instant convenience of it. The one exception was Robin Hole. When he arrived in the same house, a term after me, I was detailed to take care of him, show him round and generally look after him for the first fortnight. We discovered we had interests in common other than work, games, and the House Spirit with which I was instructed to imbue him.

'There was a further connection between us, Robin and me, a territorial one. His family came from Warwickshire, mine had done until my father's job as a professional diplomat took him wandering around the world with my mother, often leaving me during the school holidays in the care of an uncle and aunt who lived in the West Country.

'Robin was a good games player; I was not, but we had other interests in common, fishing for example. We went fishing together on College Pond, a ten-acre lake, and watched duck flighting in at dusk to join the semi-tame residents who lived there. We had both started shooting by then during the holidays, and wished we were allowed to bring our guns back to school with us.

'In connection with those duck, I remember one episode which, when we heard about it from what were usually regarded as reliable sources, Robin and I condemned with all

52

the vigour of a couple of politicians who had not thought of the idea themselves. It seemed that a boy we knew in another house had spent a great deal of time feeding the duck on College Pond until they came trustingly to his call. During the final week of the Christmas term, he somehow acquired a shotgun (quite a feat in itself, we grudgingly admitted), paid a final visit to College Pond, called the duck, and for an end of term feast shot as many as could be accounted for with both barrels of a four-ten.

'Our disapproval of this unsporting behaviour, had we been honest enough to admit it, was matched by a sneaking admiration for boldness in getting to grips with those duck which we just sat and watched. The boy in question later became a general.

'My friendship with Robin Hole extended beyond the termtime, and I started going for a week or so most holidays to stay at Frampton, his parents' home in Warwickshire. Although my father came from the other side of the county, my godfather had been the rector of the nearby village, and before he died I remembered being brought over to the rectory for tea; he was a bachelor and was looked after by a housekeeper. On one occasion he gave me a bible which I swapped at my prep school for a camera. But that was well before the Holes came to live at Frampton. My godfather had been dead for some years, I may have mentioned him to Robin, I cannot remember.

'Frampton was a small estate, a real jewel of a place, all woods and pasture, set apart from the urban sprawl of the West Midlands. The house, square, red-brick and not especially beautiful, was nevertheless wholly at one with its surroundings. Mr and Mrs Hole made it seem very friendly.

'On one visit Robin's mother got me on my own, and gently probed me as to whether he had his leg pulled much at school on account of his initials and name. She would not insult my boyish sensitivity by direct questioning, and the way she guided the conversation was a masterpiece of tactful interrogation. She gave nothing of her own intuition away, kept me off the hook as best she could, and yet appealed to me for reassurance. That reassurance was easy enough to give. Other boys only made the mistake of taking Robin's good nature for granted once, I said. Knowing her son's character, I suspect she guessed as much.

'Robin's father must have been as well aware as his mother of the cross their son would have to bear at school with those initials. A few days later I got an indication of this, almost an explanation, as it were, meant for me as Robin's friend.

'We had been shooting rabbits, and were sauntering back towards the house. None of us had said anything for sometime, each content with his own thoughts. Mr Hole broke the silence. "This is Shakespeare country, David, remember the quotation from *Romeo and Juliet*: "What's in a name? That which we call a rose, by any other name would smell as sweet." Mr Hole continued, "The name of Sherston smells pretty sweet to me at moments like this, despite what it may have done for Robin." By now we had reached the house. "I'll tell you why this evening," he said.

'"Robin told me that you had a godfather who was a parson here," began Mr Hole after we had had tea, "his name I think would be Henry Radford. I'll tell you a story about him."

I knew that the Reverend Henry Radford had been the last of a clerical dynasty spanning three generations in this area of Warwickshire, but I did not know a great deal else about him, or indeed why he had been chosen to be my godfather, unless it was on the expectation of a little legacy when he died. He had been what is, or rather was, referred to as a sporting parson, and that must have called for a certain amount of private means. I did hear my father once say that God must have been short of a gun the day Henry Radford died!

'The Frampton Estate, said Robin's father, had been left in trust to Robin's mother by her uncle, the late Mr. William Sherston. Robin's father had hardly known William Sherston, or indeed Frampton, until he came to live there when William Sherston died. But he had known my godfather, Parson Radford.

54

'When Robin's parents came to Frampton after the war, one of their earliest visitors was the Reverend Mr Henry Radford. Of course they had heard about Parson Radford, heard that their benefactor Mr Sherston had not often been seen in church, but the Parson was often seen up at the Hall — especially when they were shooting. It struck the newcomers to Frampton that the relationship between Mr Sherston and Parson Radford had more in it of things temporal than spiritual. It also struck them that the Reverend Radford's visit on that occasion had a purpose to it, and was not just a friendly introduction; he seemed to be somehow measuring them up against his expectations.

'I was beginning to get the impression that Mr and Mrs Hole knew a good deal more about my godfather than I did myself.

'After that initial visit in late summer, they didn't see much of Mr Radford socially. Mrs Hole was fully occupied in putting the house to rights after fifty years of bachelor occupation, and her husband busy getting to grips on her behalf with managing the estate. Parson Radford — as I was beginning to think of him — was there for the meeting whenever they met, which in a small rural community was quite often; but seldom for long. For the Holes there was too much else going on for them to think about dinner-parties and that sort of thing. Besides which the Parson was a good deal older than themselves, and apart from the common denominator of Mr William Sherston, they had little else in common — or so it seemed to the Holes. However, whenever they did meet, it struck Mr Hole that the Parson contrived to bring the subject of shooting into the conversation, usually with specific reference to Frampton.

'The shoot at Frampton had been old William Sherston's pride and joy. It would have been sheer ingratitude to let it go to pot. Apart from this feeling, Mr Hole could think of no pleasanter way of entertaining his friends than by asking them to come and shoot, an opportunity which until then had been denied him.

'So the shoot was kept going in much the same way as it had been under the old régime, to begin with anyway. With the passing of the years changes were made, but as the first volley of shots broke the stillness of the Frampton woods for the first time each year, Mr Hole said he sensed the shadowy presence of William Sherston watching over his shoulder.

'That first shooting season at Frampton posed the question of who Mr Hole should ask; some of his old friends of course, but what about the locals? He consulted the keeper for advice, and the two of them came up with a list of possibles. As an afterthought the keeper added, 'You'll be asking Parson Radford, of course." Mr Hole would have asked him anyway. It was as if by some higher command, transmitted mind to mind, that the name of the Reverend Henry Radford was included amongst the names of the guns to be invited.

'On the day that Parson Radford came to shoot there were eight guns out; a mixture of locals from the list of 'ought-to-be-asked' and a couple of old friends. Amongst the 'ought-to-be-asked' was a newly-appointed county court judge who had come to live in the area, and who was terribly keen on shooting. So said Mrs Hole, who had got to know the judge's wife. Mr Hole said he felt rather like one imagines a football manager feels when he takes over at a new club, but his concern was less with skilled performers, more with team spirit. Today he thought he had got it about right, no outstanding players as far as he knew, and no prima donnas who expected always to be in the limelight – again so far as he knew. But he had done all the homework he could beforehand. The only person he had not been able to run any sort of check on was the judge, and Henry Radford's credentials he had been brainwashed into taking for granted.

'As I listened to Robin's father, I got the impression that the events of that day were still very fresh in his mind.

'When he first came to Frampton he had been told by the keeper that old Mr Sherston had always placed the guns himself, saying it was the best way to ensure that everyone got a fair share of the shooting. But that method rather depended on knowing both the guns and the coverts, which Mr Hole then did not. There are numbering systems which ensure that everyone stands next to someone different each drive. The trouble with that is that the guns forget their number, or a lot of them do. For his first shoot at Frampton Mr Hole had settled for the simple system of moving up two each drive.

'The numbers drawn that morning meant little to Mr Hole. It was only when he began dispatching each to his peg that he became aware of who was standing next to who. Number 1 was Parson Radford, and number 2 was the judge; the others followed, without any particular significance, then or later.

'Having shown all the guns to their pegs for the first drive, he was walking back to where he intended to stand before blowing his whistle for the drive to begin, when he heard a shot ring out. Mr Hole turned in his tracks. He could see Henry Radford with his gun broken, in the process of reloading. Nothing else untoward seemed to have happened, so he quickly blew his whistle for the drive to begin. When it was over nobody said anything about the solitary shot ahead of the starting signal, the parson offered no explanation, and so Mr Hole left it at that.

'At the conclusion of the second drive, he was somewhat surprised to be approached by the judge who took him aside, apologised, and said he must go home straight away. Naturally Mr Hole enquired what was wrong, and was told that the judge suffered from recurrent bouts of malaria. He felt one coming on now, and knew that it would make him quite incapable of concentrating on anything, let alone shooting. Would his host forgive him for calling it a day, and apologise to the other guns on his behalf?

'"Of course" said Mr Hole, thinking it was a strange time and place for malaria to strike.

'A brief word to the other guns, who were standing round after the drive, informed them of the reason for the judge's premature departure. There were appropriate expressions of sympathy. Henry Radford said he thought the judge had looked a bit pale and feverish, when he had gone over at the beginning of the drive to let him know why his gun had gone off accidentally. No danger though, he had explained, the shot had gone harmlessly into the ground, could have been nasty if a chap had been careless. Best thing to do if you are feeling off-colour like that is to go home, the parson added.

'The numbering of the guns was reorganised, and they went on with the shoot.

'Experienced shooting hosts will tell you that once the guns have drawn for their places, they can visualise drive by drive who is likely to get the best and the worst of the shooting. Mr Hole was not yet in a position to hazard such a guess at Frampton. If he had been, he might have noticed that Henry Radford's new number qualified him for the best.

'As the birds flew the Parson's way he did full justice to them. He reached out and pulled screamers from the sky, not flukes but high birds perfectly well within range, that the others were missing. One drive a covey of partridges came on straight towards the guns standing back from a tall hedgerow, scattering too late as they saw the human figures. Parson Radford was on to them as they topped the hedgerow, and had one bird with each barrel before they swept between him and the next-door gun. Another drive and a woodcock flickered out along the covert's edge, flying the gauntlet of several of the guns before the Parson clipped it down in a puff of brown feathers. Each drive he got his share of the shooting, and made the best of it, so that the watching Mr Hole — he carried a gun for form's sake — could do nothing but admire such a polished performance.

'Thinking about it afterwards, Mr Hole said, it almost seemed as if the spirit of William Sherston was with his old friend that day. And with the birds too, willing them to go within range of Parson Radford's gun.

'The end of the last drive: guns collected together chatting; beaters making their way home in twos and threes; the two pheasants tied together with binder twine, the thanks and the tip. The end of a good day's shooting, and in to the house for tea. Shooting is not a sport where you should feel it necessary to go up and tell people how well they have done (or how badly, thank goodness!), but after such a spectacular performance as Henry Radford's, Mr Hole felt it would be churlish not to say something to him, especially as the host.

'He found the old parson strangely quiet when he went up to talk to him, but the tea, warmth, and genuine appreciation of his performance did their work, and Henry Radford began to come out of whatever private place his mind had occupied. It did not therefore seem an embarrassing question to ask, and Mr Hole asked it. Why that single shot before the first drive began? The Reverend Henry Radford, Mr Hole recalled, looked down into the cup he was holding as if reading his fortune in the tea-leaves there. He said, without looking up, that his gun had gone off accidentally, must have been the firing-pin sticking out when the breech was closed, he supposed. Then he looked up from his tea-cup, directly at Mr Hole, who remembered his words exactly: "Don't forget I've shot here for years, my boy. Marvellous shoot for seven guns, useless for eight." And he winked.

'The Reverend Henry Radford never shot at Frampton again. Shortly after "Parson Radford's Red-Letter Day", as it is recorded in the remarks column of the game book, he had a stroke and died. When he heard the news, the old keeper, standing outside his cottage in the evening as the pheasants were going up to roost, remarked wryly to Mr Hole, "Hear them pheasants, Sir, reckon they know the owd parson's gorn where 'e carn't git at 'em no longer".

'In his will Henry Radford had left a legacy of five thousand pounds to Robin Sherston Hole to be made available to him on his sixteenth birthday, so that, as it was stated in the will, "He may be provided with a suitable gun, may learn to shoot like a gentleman, and the name of Sherston may be associated with Frampton for a further generation".

' "Tomorrow is Robin's sixteenth birthday," said Mr Hole.

'He was my godfather, I thought to myself, and what did I ever get from him? Tea and a bible.'

Chapter Seven

Hugh Bird

The next story has a personal note to it. I'd known the person who told it, Hugh Bird, since he was a boy. He once came to stay with us at the decrepit old mill house where we lived then. There were rats all over the place, inside and out (one actually died entombed in the wall – and did that creature smell!). Hugh was happy shooting rats, as he was happy shooting anything else permissible. What sort of gun he used I cannot remember, any would have served. I could find an easy sympathy with him, because when I was a boy armed with an airgun, anything not proscribed by the parent – robins, thrushes, blackbirds etcetera – was fair game. The best trophy was a rabbit or a pigeon – something you could actually eat! I was a killer, and I recognised in young Hugh Bird a kindred spirit.

Hugh was an extrovert lad, his killer instinct restricted by a healthy respect – instilled in him by his father – for what might justifiably be shot, when, and how. I suspect that this early restraint, together with a thorough education in the ways of wild birds and animals, again from his father, prepared the way for a deeper interest in natural history than is common in a great many shooting men. In a nutshell, shooting and wildlife meant a great deal to young Hugh Bird, even if in those days shooting was his top priority.

Then tragedy struck. As a passenger, Hugh was seriously injured in a car crash, so seriously that he came out of it in his late teens, condemned to spend the rest of his days in a wheelchair.

One reads in the newspapers about the parents being supportive when this sort of thing happens. Well, that's one way to put it. Hugh Bird's parents set about rebuilding him. They did it with the expert assistance of those marvellous piecers-together of shattered human bodies at Stoke Mandeville. But Hugh's father and mother put the finishing touches. What he was physically incapable of doing they sought to find a means – mechanical or otherwise – of doing for him. Hugh Bird's resolution did the rest.

I see him now off and on, married, busy, involved in all manner of things including raising money for others by sponsored pushes of his wheelchair; invariably cheerful and always good company. On the occasion which I record here (as the compiler of these stories I claim it as my privilege to write the preface to this one) he was my guest at one of our dinners. I asked him to tell us how he coped with shooting after his accident. Characteristically, he told us this story instead.

'I was paralysed, as you probably know, in 1970. Thanks to an inventive and decisive father I was provided with wonderful new methods of shooting, and we worked out all kinds of ways to get a chap paralysed from the waist down out in the field again. I had a vehicle specially built for me so that I could go most places across country; we called it the Moon-buggy. Now I shoot out of an American jeep. Very successful – the jeep. The shooting varies, like most.

'But I'd like to tell you about something that happened some time ago. It's quite a funny story. My father devised a chair which was basically a wooden office chair with arms, but with the legs cut off. It was bolted to a sheet of PTFE – you're going to ask me what that is, I'll tell you in a moment – in four places and secured with wingnuts. PTFE, for those of you who are not technically-minded, is a sort of plastic substance which provides a slippery surface, so that in my case the chair could swivel. I had a pole anchored to the floor reaching up to the chair, which I held with my left hand. I held the gun in my right hand, and I had the cartridges in my pocket as usual.

'Using this chair, I successfully shot some duck on the farm at home. Then we took it to Uist with the idea of getting down to a little serious wildfowling; unfortunately there weren't all that many duck, but the chair served its purpose well. It needed one or two minor modifications; the swivelling system was not smooth enough, neither was the platform on which the chair stood large enough.

'A year or two later, my father very kindly took me up to Islay, off the west coast of Scotland. A great experience, which I enjoyed enormously. It was the second year I'd used my chair, by this time a refined piece of equipment. It was exhilarating to feel confidence in this chair, which gave shooting back to me again.

'We found where the geese were feeding one morning – on a plain grass field surrounded by a stone wall. There were a lot of geese in that field, whitefronts and barnacles. I should say at this point that it was before there was a total clampdown by the RSPB on the shooting of geese in Islay, a decision which I cannot see was really justified, and which caused me to resign from the Society. But that's by the way; I'm not here to air my views on conservation. A very, very wonderful place Islay, very wonderful indeed, and full of geese and duck.

'We got up early the next morning, not the sort of early you have to be when you're flighting duck, but in good time to give ourselves a chance, but with little or no wind it was a bad morning to flight geese. The plan was that I was to be placed in the field, in a corner by a gateway, and left there for an unspecified period to wait for anything put up by the other members of the party who would be operating further afield. They made sure that I was properly equipped with my gun and cartridges, my dog, and my lunch. The keeper put out some dead geese as decoys, then they left me. I was on my own.

'The others set off in a Land-Rover to quarter the island scaring geese. As an exercise this was successful in its first object of stirring up the geese. Getting them to fly in my direction was never envisaged as a realistic option. That was left open to chance. Even if any of the harried geese did come my way, with the almost total lack of wind there was that day, the odds were that they would be well out of range. Or so I thought. I suppose my father was thinking along the lines of the old Scottish ghillie who pithily remarked to his 'gentleman' when the latter eventually caught a salmon, "There's fules in the water as well as oot o' it". My father's thinking proved to be correct.

'Left on my own I was happy. I heard geese all around me. By this time it was about nine o'clock on an almost springlike morning. A flock of about two thousand barnacles passed high overhead, a wonderful sight with the sun glinting on their black and white bellies. With the prospect of a long wait, I checked that everything was in reach of me; my gun and my cartridges were there, of course, ready, but where were my sandwiches and my beer? If I couldn't reach them I was stuck without, until someone came to relieve me. And I do get terribly hungry out in the open. There they were, just, and only just, within reach of my chair. Contentedly I relaxed to await the outcome of the morning, even if that were only sitting listening to and watching the geese, and drinking in the crisp morning sunshine.

'As I say, I do get terribly hungry, and there seemed no reason why I should not dig in to my beer and sandwiches. When you're stuck in the middle of nowhere, immobile and inactive, time stands still and an empty stomach talks loudest. I began to position myself for a grab at the sandwiches, which in my case is not the simple matter it is for most people. Then I heard the unmistakable gabble of approaching geese.

'There they were, coming over the wood in front, and low, straight towards me − whitefronts. Three or four teal passed over me very, very fast, obviously going from pond to pond, and they went straight across my corner of the field. Though the teal were well within range, I didn't see them until it was too late to shoot; just as well, I might have been tempted, but I was in the grip of goose fever. There were only a dozen or so of the whitefronts, perhaps attracted by the decoys the keeper had put out for me. Fortunately I had checked that he hadn't left the dead decoy geese – also whitefronts – with the legs showing from underneath the bodies. I'm sure he was too experienced a man to do this, but it was worth checking; the approaching whitefronts would have noticed the deception in a flash. Any blood showing, too, would have been a complete turnoff. And on they came, those tantalising whitefronted geese.

'I checked that the old threes were in both barrels. They were. I eased my gun over the edge of the hide – if you could call my squat a hide, with the camouflage netting draped around me like a shroud – when a perfect oaf on the nearby farm started up a tractor. Of what concern was it to me that some local crofter had a living to make from his few miserable acres, why should he choose this moment to start up his bloody tractor and scare away MY geese? Vroom... vroom...vroom...went the tractor, and the incoming geese thought better of it, checked in their descent, and began to gain height and speed to get themselves out of trouble. They obviously did not see me as the trouble spot, because they flew straight over me.

'I could just get a goose – a right and left if I was dead lucky.

'I aimed my first barrel at the leading bird, which was directly overhead, and fired. As I suspect practically everyone round this table knows, having killed the first bird you've shot at, you instinctively look for your next and concentrate on that. It's automatic. I saw the leading goose – the one I'd fired at – fold, and looked for my next shot. It sounds so deliberate describing it all now, words don't match the speed with which these things happen. I suppose I must have been just about to lock to the next bird and get off my second barrel when, out of the very corner of my eye, I saw the shot goose falling. It was coming absolutely plumb straight at my head.

'A whitefronted goose is no snipe, it weighs anything between four and five pounds, and as I said earlier there wasn't a breath of wind that day to deflect the course of the falling goose. Just as well I hadn't started on the Carlsberg Special Brew I'd brought with my lunch; it might have delayed my reactions. As it was all I had time to do was to shift my head a few inches before the goose struck. It hit the arm of my chair. It was a high goose, and by the time it hit the arm of my chair it was falling like a thunderbolt. If it had hit my neck, there's no doubt about it, I wouldn't be here talking to you tonight, I'd have been a goner.

'Having failed to break my neck, the wretched goose bounced off the arm of my chair and thwacked in amongst my sandwiches and the said Carlsberg Special Brew, bursting the can so that it hissed out its contents like a burst water main all over my hide and the dog. The goose had missed the dog by a hair's breadth, for that at least the poor old boy had to be grateful, even if he did get soaked in Special Brew! Surveying the damage, I saw that some of the sandwiches had miraculously remained intact, but tantalisingly they had somehow been jolted out of my reach. I toyed with the idea of getting the dog to retrieve the sandwiches, but discarded it as impracticable; no dog — however well trained — could be expected to reach such a peak of self-discipline. He sat there drooling over the good things displayed so invitingly a foot or so from his nose, and if I'd felt more equably disposed I should have praised him for his self-restraint. As it was I simply glowered at the poor creature as the pangs of hunger, accentuated by the adrenalin pumping through my system, began to gnaw. The goose alone, stone dead from the moment I shot it, lay surprisingly undamaged within my reach.

'I knew it was most unlikely that I would see another human being until three-thirty in the afternoon.

'I tried with the end of the gun barrel to get hold of the nearest sandwich. No, no luck. I mouthed at the dog, pleaded with him, "go on, bring it, bring it, BRING IT YOU BLOODY DOG, BRING THE SANDWICH". He misunderstood me. Buggerrr! The sandwich had gone down, that left only two. Again I reached out with the gun barrel for the nearest of the two remaining sandwiches, and succeeded only in getting a muzzle full of mud. I cleaned the gun. It was instinctive, and it took my mind off food, at least for the time that it took to extract the mud from the gun.

'Eight-thirty in the morning it had been when my father and the others left me, my father in his inimitable way jumping in the jeep with the keeper, now that he'd seen me into position impatient to be off. "G'bye, old boy, see you about three-thirty, we'll come and pick you up." "Bye Dad." And now it was half-past two in the afternoon.

'And then I forgot about the sandwiches. Forgot them in the excitement of seeing another goose heading for me, a lone one this time, and I shot it. I don't remember anything remarkable about the shooting of that goose, perhaps the earlier excitement had robbed me of some of the thrill, perhaps it was that I didn't kill it dead. The goose planed down with half-closed wings, and pitched short of a wood three or four hundred yards away. The old dog must have been watching the bird, reckoning that at last he might actually get some work to do. He'd had a difficult day so far, and he'd reacted with commendable sangfroid to my excesses brought on by frustration and hunger. Now it was his turn to have some of the action. A "hi-lost" from me, and off he went, over the wall surrounding the field, and straight as a die in the direction of the wood. I saw him check and put his nose to the ground, and then he disappeared into the wood. About ten minutes later out he came with the goose in his mouth. Despite age and arthritis he jumped the wall like a two-year-old, and as he came closer to me I could see by the set of his tail that he was pleased with himself. He delivered the goose to my hand; by this time it was dead. He looked up at me as if to say, 'There you are, you're not the only one with problems, and I did rather better than you this time'.

'It wasn't long after that when I heard the Land-Rover. I looked at my watch, it was three-thirty exactly.

'Gentlemen,' said Hugh, 'if I close my eyes [he did, we didn't] I can call to mind a complete retake of that day. I've told you about it, as best I can, but what's in my brain-box is far more vivid; not in any way photographic, but sort of imprinted there for me to read, and to see, as I saw it that day on Islay.

'Now of course we all have memories like this, but speaking personally, I don't have too many such vivid ones that have to do with shooting, and I sometimes wonder why this particular one stands out so. Of course, there was the drama of what happened that day, but on reflection I think it stands out so strongly because it marks a turning point in my enjoyment of shooting, a realisation of what I could have missed and what I didn't appreciate until then. Before my accident I had the killer instinct; after it, when I realised I would be able to shoot again, I became rather more philosophical about what I wanted out of shooting. It certainly wasn't just to kill birds and animals.

'It struck me one day that if that falling goose had actually hit me in the neck and I'd been a goner, I might have had some awkward questions to answer when I came up before St Peter.

'"Hugh Bird," the serene voice might have said, with a distinctly steely note to it, "I have your record here," (tapping with a long forefinger a heavy vellum sheet) "I must say that for a relatively short time on earth it is not a very good one. I think it is appropriate that we should take first the offence which brought you here, the particulars of which are that in the name of sport you attempted to shoot one of God's creatures, namely a whitefronted goose. What have you to say to the charge?"

'"Well, your Worship...your Holiness I mean, since the goose did actually kill me, I should like to plead self-defence."

'"What utter nonsense! I have heard some damned − a slip of the tongue, my mind was on something else − some feeble excuses over the centuries, and yours is as feeble as most. If you cannot do better than that, young man, I'll send you down straight away." I had visions of the attendant angels twitching their wings in a meaningful way at these stern words, and I thought again. I knew I had to tell the truth.

"'It's like this, your Holiness, I couldn't help it — shooting at that goose, I mean (they'd have the one I shot already chalked up against me) — I was just doing what came naturally. It's the genes you see, the genes I was handed out at birth. Weren't we all programmed to hunt for our living? I know the city-dwellers have their meat killed for them, but for those of us who live in the country — well it seems so natural. Is it really such a sin?"

"'Well, my son, excess is a sin," the voice had taken on a kindlier note, "and if you had been guilty of that I should have sent you to join a syndicate which I have rented down below where they shoot low pheasants all day, and talk about it all night. As it is on this occasion I shall caution you against excesses of all kinds, and now we shall move on to the next of your offences..." '

Chapter Eight

Guardian Angel

'I was walking home after flighting pigeons. I let Sam, my dog, run on ahead of me to stretch his legs, and then something rather extraordinary happened. I had just reached a disused railway line which you walk along for a couple of hundred yards before picking up the track which leads to where I park the car, when all of a sudden Sam came running back to me. Having reached me, he turned and began to growl, not an angry growl, but a low vibrating sound deep down in his throat. He stood stock still, his eyes fixed straight ahead of him. Then he sat down and began to whine. There was nothing that I could detect to account for this inexplicable behaviour on the part of my usually placid old labrador, so I walked on, thinking he would follow when he had got over whatever it was that was bothering him. I had gone perhaps fifty yards, and turned round to see if Sam was following, but there he was sitting exactly where I had left him. I called; he wouldn't budge. I'd never known him behave like this before, so I walked back to see what was the matter.

'As I got near to where the dog was sitting, he took absolutely no notice of my approach, his whole attention seemed to be concentrated on something behind me. By now the light was beginning to fail. For the first time I felt uneasy; Sam was seeing — experiencing — something which I was not, at least not until now.

'What happened next really did make me want to get back to the car as quickly as possible. As I put my hand on the dog's head and began to talk to him, he snarled at me. Sam, who had been with me for eight years, and who, though I say it myself, worshipped me, to snarl like that! I withdrew my hand, but continued to talk to him. Then Sam put back his head and gave a long drawn-out howl. I have never heard a wolf howl, but I imagine that despairing animal cry was how starving wolves howl for food. Again I put my hand on the dog's head. I could feel him trembling all over. Then his body relaxed, I could sense the tension go out of him. He got up, shook himself as if to be rid of something unpleasant, and danced around me, getting as near to jumping up as he dared. We walked quickly back together to the car.

'I've never known a dog behave like that before or since. I thought about it afterwards, and wondered if Sam had suffered some kind of fit, canine DTs, if there is such a thing, something which affected his brain. I don't believe it. Sam lived to sleep his way to death five years later. I have come to the conclusion that he was simply scared out of his wits. But by what? And what about my reaction? Was it the place or the dog's behaviour which put the wind up me?'

That was Peter Kendall's story. In response, you might have expected someone to quote from *Hamlet*, 'There are more things in heaven and earth...'. Instead, his final question met with another quotation; it was so apt that I looked it up to make sure I had got it right:

'In the rabbinical book, it saith
The dogs howl, when, with icy breath
Great Sammael, the Angel of Death,
Takes through the town his flight!'

Archie Kingair spoke the words. He added, 'Longfellow, "Golden Legend". For "town", Peter, substitute railway line'.

Archie Kingair was the grandson of an expatriate Scot, quite a famous one, Laidlaw Kingair, the celebrated advocate-turned-politician, who is equally well-known for the crime stories he wrote under the name of Iain Laidlaw. Archie made no claim to fame himself, or on the patronage of his distinguished grandparent, but he did claim − unconsciously perhaps − the visionary streak of the Celt. He was a quiet, unassuming man of impeccably good manners. He was interesting to listen to and a good listener. In a crowd he was inclined to be silent, and it was unusual for him to speak up at our dinners.

Archie continued, 'I believe that people can sometimes leave their mark on places, and I do not necessarily mean by association. If you know that something quite dramatic happened at a particular spot, a battle or a murder, for instance, it's easy enough for the imagination to do the rest. You know what happened there, you imagine it happening. I'm looking at it the other way round. You don't know what happened, but somebody is trying to remind you. He, or she, may not be able to get through to you direct, only to a simpler mind, a dog's mind, perhaps!'

I remember there was a pause at this point, a moment of uncertainty about what was coming next; like politics or religion, the supernatural was not a subject anyone had chosen to air before at one of our dinners. Neither were we accustomed to Archie Kingair talking to us collectively. I for one wondered why he should choose to do so on this occasion. He must have sensed the mood of the moment, because he continued: 'I once had an experience which I think proves my point. That is, if you are interested in hearing about it.'

We encouraged Archie to continue. I record the rest of his story without interruption.

'Hector, Professor Sir Hector Kingair, Uncle Hector (though I never called him that) was born in 1918. He was educated at Eton and Oxford, served in a cavalry regiment, survived − one of the few who did − Red Beach at Dieppe in 1942, and got back to England from where he sent the legendary postcard: "Have been for a trip to the seaside. It was very hot and I did not like it".

'When the war ended, he became a journalist, and worked

71

as defence correspondent on two national newspapers before becoming involved with Lord Ramsgate and his Defence of the Realm Movement, a privately financed think-tank set up to study, and to influence, future Government policy. Together they founded NCLS, the National College for Logistic Studies, and Hector Kingair became its first Principal. He was also Pitcairn Professor of Logistics at Oxford. He wrote a number of books, including a marvellous life of Abraham Lincoln, and had completed the first volume of a study of post-war European politics when he died.

'Alone of my grandfather's children, Hector inherited his father's intellect, his work ethic, and his seriousness. He did not have an easy time as Principal of the NCLS, but then he wasn't a man who wanted life on easy terms. He would keep telling the older generation of admirals and generals that their experiences during the Second World War were irrelevant. However, several of the younger generation at the top of the military hierarchy considered him to be the most important political and military strategist of his era. "A prophet is not without honour, save in his own country" – Hector Kingair's name is still almost revered in America and Europe as a progressive strategic thinker.

'He was blunt, impatient, and seemingly (though not in fact) short-tempered. On one celebrated occasion he told Black Rod, at that time the Victor of Alamein, to mind his manners.'

As Archie was talking, I remember thinking to myself, this is a bit of a change from the usual stuff we get at these dinners: anecdotes, funny stories, feats, but always about shooting. This was something different. I welcomed it, and looking around the faces it seemed the others did as well. Archie appeared to sense that he was getting carried away by the memory of his uncle, and said, 'I'm sorry to go on about my uncle, but you have to understand the sort of man he was, before you can begin to weigh up the evidence for what I swear actually happened to me that day out shooting.' He need not have looked for reassurance, there was a pause, a brief mutter of conversation connected mostly with the refilling of glasses, and we settled down to listen again.

'So a paragon, this uncle of mine – gifted, hardworking, knowledgeable, a fine writer, a wonderful father to his own children, and yet a man who seemed as though the cares of his knowledge – a world gone mad with nuclear-equipped political power – had made troubled, serious, and even physically bowed. He was over six foot tall, but he stooped so much that he invariably looked out from under his eyebrows. Paragon or paradox? For all his distinction he could be difficult, having sometimes a stern and forbidding manner, and a capacity to rub people up the wrong way. But then he lived between the dictators and the dissolution of empire.

'But beneath this exterior lurked the kindest and most human man I have ever known.

'Hector loved gardens and books, he liked stupid jokes and puns, and he listened to us youngsters, myself and my four brothers and sisters, all in our teens, as though we might actually have something interesting to say.

'Then, when I was eighteen and my brother Andrew, the youngest of the five of us, fourteen, our mother died suddenly. I suppose we were an unconventional lot, because we decided – like some junior soviet – that rather than go and live with anyone else, we would continue to live together in our old house on our own. Surprisingly perhaps, our decision was accepted, a trust was set up to provide for us, and Hector Kingair, my uncle, became our guardian.

'Someone had to run the house on a day-to-day basis (we tried housekeepers but that didn't work – maybe it was too much to expect anyone to stand the strain!) so I left my job and became resident caretaker. Hector and I then came into contact a lot.

'If any of us young Kingairs – me especially – didn't know it before, we learnt then that here in our uncle was a man who, however fierce his exterior, had a great kindness within, a lurking sense of humour ready to be out when the occasion arose – which it frequently did with us – and a sense of duty

73

over and above what might reasonably have been expected of him. That sense of duty was to ensure that the five of us were provisioned for life: with cash – however tight that might be, with guidance, with sound advice, and with moral support whenever we should need it. A rather special relationship, I think you will agree.

'But I like to think we gave something back in return, unconsciously though it may have been at the time. His own children were dutiful and clever, but perhaps somewhat in awe of him. We provided him with amusement, independence of his own family, and the surprise factor in a well-ordered life. And we teased him blind. He called us 'The Commune' because, he said, we were self-sufficient and self-supporting. Unlike those he worked with, he also quickly found it was impossible to get us to adopt one of his suggestions or follow one of his orders if we did not choose to do so. If we gave him a hard time, he never made us (or anyone else) feel that we were a cross which he had to bear.

'We loved our uncle, too, for his helplessness in practical matters. His attainments and distinction were set at nothing when it came to something like pruning a fruit tree. He was quite capable of sawing through the branch on which he was standing. In fact he removed two of his toes with a Flymo, giving himself a permanent limp, and when he discovered the labour-saving potential of the chain-saw we feared for an even more disastrous mutilation. In the event we managed to restrain him only when he had felled four of the trees he was intent on pruning, torn his trousers and gashed his knee – God only knows what prevented full amputation! Like many impractical men he loved gadgets and machines. I'm sure he almost memorised the maker's instructions, but when it came to putting them into practice he was completely lost. Cars, too, had their problems for him. Once, when driving me back after having given me a long and furious lecture on "Being Responsible", he ran straight into the back of another vehicle.

'And so at last we come to shooting. As you might imagine from what I've just said, Hector Kingair was a hopeless shot, and a dangerous one. He was in the position of being joint-host on our family shoot, or he would never have been asked — a second time. He shot me at least twice, with one near-miss. On that occasion I was heading up a long narrow strip of scrub, which the other guns, walking in line, were blanking in. A pheasant got up and flew low straight towards me. My uncle fired at the bird as soon as it became airborne. Fortunately I had taken note of Hector's position, as, from bitter experience of the danger involved, I usually did by then, and threw myself flat on the ground. I heard a shout of "For God's sake, Hector, be careful, Archie's right in line with where you've just shot." And the reply, "Don't make such a fuss Eddie, I can see him quite clearly."

'Hector never unloaded his gun crossing any form of obstacle to his progress, and once, who could forget it, his shooting-stick broke and he fell over backwards, discharging both barrels, fortunately with as little damage to human life as they normally had when he was pointing them purposefully at a pheasant.

'Despite these defects, my uncle looked the picture of a professional when he came out shooting. He wore beautifully cut tweeds with long leather gaiters, and Lobb shooting boots; on his head one of those broad-brimmed felt hats made pre-war by Lock. And his accoutrements, too, were early twentieth-century Bond Street: they included a leather-cased thermos flask, and silver sandwich box which stood out in contrast to the plastic and Tupperware containers produced by the rest of us when we had a picnic lunch. I remember he also had a silver whistle, which seemed to be permanently blocked.

'Our old keeper, Billy Nuttal, followed Hector everywhere out shooting in the additional role of minder, and therefore managed to limit the amount of damage to life and limb of which my uncle was capable if left unattended. On one occasion Harry physically flung himself on one of our guests as the questing barrels sought out yet another head-height target. The keeper had also to look for what Hector had shot

75

at, with intent to kill. His cue was invariably the shout, "I think that one's a runner, Billy", following the double-tap of both barrels and a pheasant seen maintaining its course with motionless outstretched wings. Billy Nuttal would dutifully go off, wondering for how long he dare leave his master unattended whilst making the ritual search.

'Hector had a dog, a black labrador bitch which he had "trained himself". If ever I saw a dog which would rather have been reading Proust or studying metaphysics, it was Gloss. She was dutiful and certainly not arrogant, but alone of labradors she was not interested in food, game, or other dogs, and she possessed the questing air of a kindly, absent-minded academic who has already lost all three pairs of his spectacles that morning. They suited each other perfectly. Being a liberal to the core, Hector never gave the dog orders; doing so he would have regarded as intolerably autocratic. Instead he would say, "Gloss, I wonder if you would mind plunging into that thicket and taking a look — I think I've got a runner in there." Gloss would mosey off good-naturedly, and search absent-mindedly for a bird which was not there. Perhaps both of them knew it; that was their understanding.

'Then, one winter's day, the tall bent figure was gone. Hector Kingair had had his last day's shooting. There would be other days for us, but Parsley Woods, our shoot in Oxfordshire, would no longer echo to the unmistakable shout of, "I think that one's a runner, Billy". We of The Commune had lost our Life President. Not yet sixty, death came for him one night when he was alone; he must have suffered from one of the blackouts which had plagued him ever since a jeep crash in the final year of the war. He choked in his sleep, and died. We went to the funeral, the members of The Commune, the five of us standing in the pew behind the immediate family. To them he was the next of kin, husband or father, to us he was our friend. And we mourned his leaving us. I was the only one who as, God is my witness, was ever permitted to see him again.

'We had anticipated that the first shoot of the season at Parsley following Hector's death would be difficult to get through without the depressing feeling for each of us that we were looking for him, only to be reminded that he was no longer there. Since he had been happy amongst us in the woods that he had left behind − perhaps the one place of true contentment in his complicated life − we were determined to try to make that day a happy one in his memory. In the event we succeeded pretty well. We had a good start, for it was one of those early winter mornings which stand the season of the year on end with its beauty: a touch of frost on the ground, the morning mist clearing to allow shafts of sunlight to lance through the trees and strike shadows down the rides; an invigorating day without the chill of winter yet to come. A good day to go shooting.

'Parsley itself is in the heart of England, and even if you've never been there before, you have to be an unimaginative creature indeed not to appreciate the seduction of a place so steeped in history. You can feel it around you, an oak tree which must have seen Cavalier and Roundhead pass beneath on the springy turf. Look out over the flat plain which once took in an ancient forest of 4,000 square miles, and you wonder what manner of man and beast lived there in the days of pre-history. It's a mysterious place and we love it, and have done so for three generations since we first came there. But back to the present.

'Once we had all met again in the familiar surroundings of the stone-built farmhouse at the end of the muddy lane, the puddles crackling that day with the thin ice breaking as you drove over them, thoughts gave way to talk: picking up threads lost over the months, the prospects for the day ahead, and so forth. By mutual consent it seemed, though every one of us must have been thinking of him, Hector's name was never mentioned.

'And so we all moved off to the first drive, and if any of us thought of Hector Kingair, it was in the quieter moments between the shooting.

'On the third drive — usually a good one — I was at the corner of a wood with all the other guns lined out to my right. I was the only one covering the ride to my left, until the gun walking along it ahead of the beaters came up to stop at his position twenty-five yards away. I hadn't shot very well so far, but that didn't bother me a great deal; it was a beautiful day, and as you might expect on a shoot like our little family affair no one much minded how well you shot — except poor Billy Nuttal the keeper, who was stuck with our performance anyway.

'Years of shooting at Parsley have taught me the habit of constantly being on the lookout for stops, stray beaters, and guests who have got lost. To be fair, much of the shoot is in a big wood intersected by rides, and it's easy enough to get lost. On this occasion I checked the position of my next-door gun on the right, and made a mental note of which might be his birds and which mine, and then I glanced down the ride to my left expecting to see no one. But there was someone. It was Hector Kingair and Gloss.

'Looking back on it now, it is difficult to say if anything unusual struck me — at the time. I think not. God knows I was used enough to seeing Hector sitting like that hunched up on his shooting-stick, wrenching his gun around as if he couldn't make up his mind which way to hold it. There was the old familiar figure once again, to me so much part and parcel of the Parsley shooting scene. It was as if I had been expecting him to turn up — especially in the wrong place!

'I turned to my front again. Minutes later I looked once more. He was still there, but now swung round on his shooting-stick facing me directly, his gun resting dangerously across his knees, hat tilted forward. I could not see the eyes at that distance, but there was no doubt in my mind who they were looking at from under those shaggy brows.

'The whirr of wings overhead alerted me to the business in hand, and to the appearance of a hen pheasant which I shot at and missed. Then, moments later, a woodcock flickered out from amongst the trees. I missed that, too. I swore, and looked round, as one does, to see if the other guns had noticed. My cousin to the right of me was happily banging away. There was no one else on the ride.

'Then the full impact of what I had seen came upon me, and like a small boy in the dark I was afraid.

'There was a noise behind me, and Billy Nuttal suddenly appeared at my side. He was clearly agitated, as he only ever became if a drive went wrong. "Excuse me, Sir," he said, "but did you see which way Sir Hector went?" I looked at Billy, but neither of us said anything. It was the only time in the twenty years I knew him that he ever called me "Sir".'

Chapter Nine

Ireland, Ireland, Green and Sad

The papers that morning had been full of pictures of the troopers and horses of the Household Cavalry killed and wounded the previous day by a bomb planted by IRA terrorists. If you were an Irishman living in London, I suspect you both felt obliged, and were well advised, to keep a low profile.

I remembered the sense of outrage I felt when I heard on the news that Lord Mountbatten had been blown to pieces by the same so-called army. Of course, it was not a feeling of personal loss, but a sense of hopelessness that any man who has made his mark on history – let alone a man of Mountbatten's stature – should be laid low by a gang of criminals. I mentally cursed the Irish for spawning them.

That very morning on the radio there had been a wise old parson speaking on the religious slot they have on the *Today Programme*. He preached – rather, talked to his listeners – about this instant reaction which follows an outrage perpetrated by some ethnic group or another. Honest, decent people cry for vengeance, the speaker pointed out, and vent their spleen on anyone who happens to come from the same country as the terrorists. Naturally, events like the Hyde Park bombing cause a reaction against Irish people. This, the clergyman pointed out, was unfair, unjust, but wholly predictable. He cautioned against such un-Christian behaviour. What that parson said made me feel rather guilty.

Anyhow, it was against this background that we met for dinner that same evening.

I don't know how many other people around the table had listened to the *Today Programme* in the morning, but if some had they didn't take much notice of what the speaker said. There was a good deal of holding forth on the subject of yesterday's outrage, some of it calculated to make anyone ashamed to claim Irish descent. One particularly vitriolic outburst was so sweeping in its condemnation of all things Irish that someone had to set the record straight. Michael Mountain spoke up for the defence. This is what he said.

'I'm perfectly sure Stuffy Brewster wouldn't want us to go on like this. Besides, this isn't a political meeting, we are here to talk shooting. Fair man that he was, Stuffy would be the first to point out that whatever's happened today, and however much hate we've got stored up for the IRA, we can't solve anything by ranting about how awful the Irish are just because the IRA are Irish. If Stuffy ever served in Ireland, you can bet your life he was more interested in shooting snipe than worried about people shooting at him. I was stationed in Ulster once. Except for one occasion I haven't been back since. If I had a second chance maybe I would go back. One thing happened above all others to put me off doing so.

'In January 1981 the IRA shot dead, in the library of the house in which the family had lived for the past two hundred years, an old man of eighty-six, and his forty-seven-year-old son. They then burnt the house down. The old man was Sir Norman Stronge, his son and heir murdered with him, James; the house, Tynan Abbey in County Armagh.

'Ireland today has become a foreign country so far as the average English person is concerned,' Michael said, 'yet it's part of the British Isles. We speak exactly the same language, we have a common history − strife-torn admittedly − a common culture, and even a common currency, give or take the buying power of the punt. The Irish come over here to work amongst us, join our armed forces and fight alongside us; we intermarry, and go without passports to and fro across the Irish Sea. We both of us love the chase, whether it's with hound, gun, or fishing rod. Anglo-Saxon and Celt seem to get on well enough together — for a time. Then off comes the lid once more with some fresh act of butchery by the IRA, and Ireland is the dog which is given the bad name.

'Norman Stronge was an Irishman. His great-grandfather had been Speaker of the Irish Parliament in the eighteenth century. He himself had been Speaker of the Ulster Parliament — Stormont — for twenty-four years. I will remember him for his kindness to me, for the introduction he gave me to the brighter side of Irish life, and for the enjoyment I had as a young man shooting with him and some of his friends.

'Tynan Abbey, the Stronge family home built in 1750 and remodelled in 1816, was a rambling Gothic house full of rooms and empty of servants. My recollection is that it was bitterly cold in the winter — if you got out of range of the fire. It was also quite difficult to find your bedroom if you were staying there. The setting was perfect. You entered the drive by way of a mini-Gothic lodge, and bumped up the carriage drive (as it had remained) until you came face to face with this crenellated square Gothic mansion. To your left the park swept down to a reed- fringed lake. To the right, so far as I remember, was a tennis court, which looked disused, and then stables and outbuildings. The backdrop was of trees, tall trees. It was in those trees that we used to shoot the pigeons.

'Because of the difficulty of getting to grips with the pigeons from ground level in the woods, some platforms had been constructed high up in certain strategically selected trees. The platforms must have been a good forty foot from the ground in some cases. You climbed up a series of home-made ladders made to fit the architecture of the tree, changing from one to another, encumbered with gun, cartridge bag, and any other paraphernalia you chose for this perilous ascent. If you were like me you did not look down. The platform was relatively spacious and had a taffrail around it to prevent premature descent. Once up there it was not so bad, because the platform and the branches of the tree hid the ground beneath. You were now ready to shoot pigeons.

'The process of collecting the pigeons you shot was taken care of by someone on the ground with a dog. It was frequently necessary for the shooter up the tree to shout directions to the man on the ground with the dog as to the whereabouts of fallen birds. This was done by the good old military expedient of target identification, "Fallen pigeon, thirty yards out, ten o'clock". Or something like that. Of course, it was important for both of you to identify beforehand the nominal position of twelve o'clock.

'The pigeon shooter up his tree had a marvellous view of the surrounding countryside, and this alone was worth the perils of the ascent. If you suffered from vertigo, then this form of shooting was not for you; otherwise it could be enormous fun.

'Anyone who has ever seriously shot pigeons knows that the birds keep on the move and fly lower in a strong wind. A windy day is a good day to go pigeon shooting — even if you do happen to be forty feet up in a swaying tree.

'I once visited the *Cutty Sark*, that sleek square-rigged tea-clipper, then laid up at Greenwich. I stood on the deck and looked aloft to the mastheads, and the tracery of spars and rigging high above the narrow deck, stationary now against the moving clouds in the sky. I wondered what it must have been like to climb up to those mastheads in a heaving sea. The nearest I ever came to a remotely comparable experience was going up to the platforms in the trees at Tynan when a half-gale was blowing. But the shooting was wonderful. No poking at a slow-moving pigeon coming in to roost or to the decoy, but a swing yards ahead of the bird's beak as it came down the wind, a bang, and more often than not a clean miss, or a shout to the dog-man below, "Forty yards, ten o'clock".

'Then there were the snipe. Little boggy patches of rough grass and rushes that could hold anything from one to a dozen of them. You could either walk the bog downwind, for a snipe gets lift by taking off into the wind, then zigzags away before holding to a steady course. The trick is to shoot at a snipe as quick as you can when the bird first gets up. You can wait until the flight straightens, but by then it's usually too late and the bird is out of shot.

'Except when there was an organised snipe shoot, two or three of us would go for a morning or an afternoon's walk. If the birds turned out to be wild we would try driving them. All this required was one person to do the driving, and the others to stand downwind of the bog, concealed by whatever natural cover there was, to do the shooting. The beater would walk through the bog, hoping it was not going to suck him in above gum-boot level, maybe occasionally clapping his hands, and up would get the snipe – if there were any there. Sometimes they flew over the waiting guns, sometimes they didn't. But it was rare that we came home snipeless.

'Pheasants there were in the woods, fields and bogs around Tynan Abbey, but not many and all wild. As you know, the pheasant prefers a light sandy soil to live and breed on in the wild. The damp acres of woodland, and the rich dark humus that carpeted this part of South Armagh, provided a wet and draughty home for the hardy pheasant population that chose to live there. I'm sure Norman Stronge, whether he could afford it or not, would not have wished to add to their numbers by weakening the strain. Besides, who would want fat, reared pheasants when there was so much else more interesting to shoot that grew wild.

'You always read about the wonderful woodcock shooting they have in Ireland. I cannot remember any of those sorts of days, at Tynan or anywhere else, that give one a chance of qualifying for the award offered by Bols for getting a left and a right at woodcock. Maybe I was in the wrong part of Ireland. All I do remember was nearly being shot by an ex-Irish international rugger player on one occasion when a woodcock flitted between us. The woodcock occupied his attention like a rugger ball coming out of the scrum; I happened to be in the way.

'For all the simmering currents of religious and political strife in Ulster, which had not come to the boil then as they have today, an outsider like me was welcomed at face value, on the strength of his credentials. One of the simplest credentials to offer, in the countryside at least, was a liking for shooting, fishing, or horses. Having belatedly come to the conclusion that a horse bites at one end and kicks at the other, I was left with fishing and shooting to offer as a passport. Fishing is another story (I caught my first salmon in Ulster), but shooting gained me some form of acceptance not only by the likes of Sir Norman Stronge, but by people whose class indicators − how Norman Stronge would have hated that media-coined description − were far lower down the social scale.

'Unlike mainland England, where the foreshore between the tidemarks is about the only place where you can enjoy free shooting, there are large tracts of moorland and bog where you can go and shoot more or less for the asking. There were snipe in the bogs and the occasional grouse on the moorland.

'I went one day alone in search of grouse, and failing to find any, I met up with another lone sportsman who had actually seen grouse where we were that day. We joined forces. I cannot remember if we saw any grouse, if indeed there were any, which my companion assured me there were; I rather think not, but I reckoned he at least knew better than I where they were likely to be. He was a postman who lived locally. He offered to show me all the most likely places for grouse in the area if I cared to join him again. I did so on many occasions. I can't say it was a particularly fruitful partnership in terms of the number of grouse shot. But I'm sure my friend the postman enjoyed having someone with whom to share his sport, instead of wanting to corner what few birds there were for himself. I found this unselfishness typical in the Ulster countryside, wherever the class indicators were set.

'The postman said if I was going shooting grouse on my own I ought to have a dog, a pointer or a setter, to find them. He gave me a young Irish red setter bitch; she was called Lottie.

'Years later, I heard a friend of mine remark in a stage whisper, "A lot more people would ask Michael shooting if he'd leave that damned awful dog at home". The dog referred to was a labrador which somehow or another I had inherited. And I have to admit he did have his faults. Maybe the rot started with Lottie, because I have never been able to resist the temptation of acquiring a secondhand dog, and as a result never owned a really steady one. The truth can often hurt.

'I think Lottie must have been given me just before I left Ireland, because I cannot remember her contributing materially to the ruination of a day's sport over there. When I did take Lottie out shooting – which was not for long – she ran like a lurcher, but lacked any of the lurcher's sense of purpose.

'The few gamekeepers I met in Ulster were unlike the English variety I was used to; they neither looked the part nor necessarily acted it. One I remember in particular, not so much on account of his appearance, but because he was carrying a most unusual gun. It appeared to have a bronze coin as an integral part at the end of one of the barrels. When the opportunity arose I could not resist making some remark to him about the unusual appearance of his gun. Oh, he said unconcernedly, the barrels had got a bit thin, so he had got the local garage to braze in a bent coin where the metal had worn through.

'Sir Norman Stronge's keeper was called Drimmie. I never did know whether it was his surname or his christian name. In stature he was a small man, and fitted in at Tynan where a more august portly presence would have seemed hopelessly out of place. He was at home with the wild birds. Somehow I could not see him amongst the pheasant coops in the rearing field, or controlling the advancing sweep of well-drilled beaters. He knew his dripping woods, his bogs, and the green fields that sloped away towards the Irish border, knew them for the birds they held. Drimmie's natural instinct was finding, not mass-producing, game.

'One shooting season Sir Norman Stronge was away on a prolonged visit to Australia or New Zealand, I can't remember which, in his official capacity as Speaker of the Ulster

Parliament. He told me I could shoot at Tynan when I wanted. An act of generosity, and of trust, which I have always remembered. Many a self-important gamekeeper would have resented being lumbered with someone licensed to come and go at will. But Drimmie responded, as I'm sure his master knew he would, by treating me as one of the family. We trudged the bogs together, we shot the pigeons, me up the tree-platform, he with the dog at the bottom, and we chased the occasional pheasant. When I chose to come to Tynan Drimmie was there to welcome me as if I belonged.

'"Bandit country", they call South Armagh now, and when I read in the papers at breakfast-time of some killing by bomb or bullet which no longer hits the headlines, I often wonder what happened to my friend the postman, and to Drimmie. Maybe old age claimed them before the bandits changed their way of life.

'Casting back to my own cosy experience of Ulster remembered, the picture comes to mind of the other big white and grey houses that stood in their walled demesnes within a twenty-mile radius of Tynan Abbey. Many were still occupied by a member of the family that built them. A few stood derelict, a reminder of earlier troubled times. Unlike England, none that I can remember had been converted into hotels, flats or conference centres, so you had the impression that behind those staring windows were echoing empty rooms that waited in vain for the lights to be turned on again.

'Yet occasionally the lights were turned on, when some owner of one of these piles decided to blow a few hundred pounds on a party, usually for one of the daughters of the house. Boyfriends were at a premium, so any more-or-less eligible bachelor − including myself − got asked. We knew strong drink would be in short supply, so we took precautions by having a bottle in the back of the car for the occasional refresher.

'On one such occasion that I recall, the host was standing outside his porticoed front door, watching one or two of his departing guests having some difficulty negotiating the many stone steps that led down to the gravel sweep of the drive. "I never thought the claret cup was so strong", he was heard to mutter.

'Looking back, it seems nothing short of rank bad manners that we behaved like this. But what the host's eye did not see his purse did not have to pay for.

'One of Sir Norman Stronge's friends, and a near neighbour, was the Earl of Caledon, Field-Marshal Alexander's elder brother. He lived in an enormous house where there was a tunnel so that the servants could enter the house without being seen. He often came to shoot, and used to drive around in a little Ford Eight car. Sir Norman reckoned that insurance companies might well impose a special premium on car insurance in the immediate vicinity of Caledon where the Earl lived.

'Another shooting friend who lived on the Republic side of the border was Lord Rossmore. Sir Norman took me to shoot grouse with him.

'Before I ever went to Ireland I had come across a book at home with the title *Things I Can Tell*, written by the Lord Rossmore of the time. In today's egalitarian world, Lord Rossmore's account of the life led by him and his friends at the turn of the century would have the book banned from every radically-inclined public library in the land. I found the sheer scale of Rossmore's outrageous adventures, and the privileged eccentricities of him and his friends, fascinating to read about. I looked forward to meeting his successor.

'I only met the incumbent Lord Rossmore on two occasions. The first was at Tynan Abbey, where he shot the highest duck I have ever seen shot. I wouldn't say it was any feat of marksmanship on his lordship's part, more the unfortunate duck's chance encounter with a stray pellet at extreme range. Anyhow, the bird fell like a stone, and I don't think anyone was more surprised than Lord Rossmore. He hadn't had much shooting that day, which might explain why he shot at the duck in the first place.

'The second occasion that I shot with Lord Rossmore was

on his own grouse moor. Everything was going well until several packs of grouse flew purposefully over, far to the right of where we were standing. Nothing came over the guns at all. Then I saw a small boy pounding down the hillside to our front. He was yelling at the top of his voice, "Me lord, me lord, you'se are in the wrong butts". By this time the situation was irretrievable.

'Strangely enough, long afterwards, I read an account of the same thing happening on this very moor in the old lord's time. On this occasion it was apparently an act of revenge on the part of the beaters against a particularly unpopular gamekeeper. That story must have been picked up from old Lord Rossmore's book. But I do know from personal experience that it also happened when I shot there. I don't think it was the beaters' fault this time, though.

'I had taken a shotgun with me to the Province without any preconceived notion of what shooting I would be likely to get. I am not Irish, I had no introductions, I did not know the place. If I had been going for any length of time to Scotland, to Wales, or to another part of England where I was a stranger, I would also have taken my gun with me. But I do not think I would have been able to use it so freely, and I do not think I would have had the same experiences to look back on. Neither should I have met such a rich variety of people to welcome me.

'I said I have been back once since. It was in the mid-seventies. I was in Ulster on business. I found I had some time on my hands, so I drove over to Tynan on a Sunday, unannounced, meaning just to sneak in and have a look at the place. It was nearly twenty years since I had been there.

'I stopped at the little mini-Gothic lodge just after midday, and enquired if Sir Norman Stronge was still about. Oh yes, said the person who answered my knock, he'll be at church just now, but go on up to the house, he'll be back soon. Though I was quite unknown to the tenant of the lodge, the assumption was that Sir Norman would be pleased to see me. It was nearing Sunday lunchtime, and I was not quite so sure. I thought I could slip away unnoticed if I saw the car coming.

'I drove up the carriage drive and parked unobtrusively. The house looked empty. I got out of the car and wandered round to the side overlooking the lake. I was walking back towards my own car when I heard the sound of a car coming up the drive. I could have escaped. I knew my way round the back of the house through the stable yard and out, but somehow I didn't want to go; after twenty years I wanted to say hello again, and then go. I watched the little motor car wend its way round the big sweep of gravel until I could see the occupants. Norman Stronge was sitting in the front and his son James was driving. I could see the old man's face peering through the car window; it bore the expression, Oh God, who's this come to disturb us? The car drew up. The passenger door opened and Norman Stronge got out. The cautious look vanished immediately in an instant smile of recognition.

'Later that afternoon I drove back to Belfast. It was raining. There is nowhere so depressing as Belfast in the rain, especially on a Sunday evening.'

Chapter Ten

Tom Parry's Last Cat

'On my desk at home there is a black-and-white photograph of a smiling man in shirtsleeves and baggy plus-fours held up by braces. Across his knees is a shotgun. If you saw the photograph you might guess the man was a gamekeeper, and you would be right. It is one of those chance snaps the amateur takes which comes alive and does not look posed; it is a photograph of our old keeper, Tom Parry, who died five years ago.

'Tom's father had been my grandfather's keeper, and Tom had continued in his footsteps first with my father then with me.'

Henry Rawlinson was talking. Henry is married to my sister. They live in North Wales. I know that photograph, and I knew Tom Parry. Henry did not describe him, but I will.

Tom had one of those faces that it is difficult to age; I would have guessed he was in his late fifties, but in the twenty years I knew him he never seemed to look any younger or any older. He was a stocky thickset man who seldom appeared to be in a hurry, and conveyed the impression of solid dependability. He was deliberate in his ways and economical in his speech. But he had a most infectious smile which seemed to light up his whole face. He was a Welshman.

I have never been able to decide whether the indigenous Welsh find it easier to think in their own language, or wish to conceal what they are saying from an outsider, but when there is one other Welsh-speaking person present they speak to one another in Welsh. Tom Parry was no exception. I like to believe he found it easier to think in Welsh, but I'm not sure.

Tom had been keeper at Llandrog when old Mr Rawlinson used to rear five hundred pheasants each season, and his family and friends came to shoot them. More recently the shoot had been let, and the shooting tenant (who ran the operation commercially) reared twenty times that number for his paying guests to come and shoot. I often wonder how Tom came to grips with the change in the way the shoot was run, and with the people who came to shoot. I'm not sure he ever really did.

I remember one occasion when my brother-in-law asked me to shoot. At that time he had an arrangement with the tenant to take a couple of guns on certain days for himself and one of his friends. We duly arrived at the rendezvous. The day had apparently been sub-let to a London property developer for him to entertain some of his clients. We tried to guess what he – more likely his company – had paid for the entertainment. I remember little of the shooting; but snatches of the conversation I do remember – even now. 'Nice of you' said one of the guns to another, 'to let me use your landing-strip yesterday.' This was at the very beginning of the Oil Crisis. The talk then shifted to the vintages of claret. I didn't feel qualified to join in. Later, after we had finished shooting and were having tea, my tongue was loosened by the whisky that followed, and I ventured into conversation with the man standing next to me. It wasn't long before he cut me short with, 'Must go now, the aircraft will be ticking over on the runway waiting for me'.

This was shooting as corporate entertainment: you shoot what is paid for, and he who pays for the shooting expects to get repaid later. Henry Rawlinson and I had nothing to repay; we were outsiders. Even if the tips were rather heftier than what he had been used to in the past, I wondered how Tom Parry would fare in the service of shooting as corporate entertainment.

But I must let Henry Rawlinson get on with his own story.

'Before my father died' Henry continued, 'he decided that the shoot should be let. When I came into the place I had no wish to change this arrangement; on the contrary, I needed the revenue from the letting. But I wanted to have something of my own to offer my friends. There were about five hundred acres on one side of the river which runs through the estate where I still had the sporting rights. I thought it would not be too difficult to turn this into a shoot which I could at least call my own.

'Tom Parry remained in charge of the let shooting. He still lived in the same cottage. He still had much the same territory, less my enclave south of the river. Yet times had changed for Tom. How much for the better or for the worse, I didn't know, and I didn't ask. I did know that he had a house to live in and a regular wage, because I provided both. It was part of the shooting tenancy agreement.

'It was fortunate for me that Tom's retirement from service in corporate shooting should coincide with my venture into the loss-making side of the business. Tom Parry came back to me as part-time keeper, and together we set about building up the alternative shoot at Llandrog.

'We had our disagreements, Tom and I, as to how we should go about building up the shoot, seldom over the method but occasionally over the means. Having settled on the number of birds we would rear, and I having paid for them, there was a certain amount of wrangling about the amount of corn needed to feed them. Evidently the restrictions now in force were far more severe than what Tom had become used to, and he found it difficult to accept that any form of rationing should be necessary. I tried to explain the economic factors of running a shoot, and that it was no longer possible to pass on to well-heeled customers the cost of the corn. But with Tom pheasants came first, and I don't think he quite accepted my explanation — judging from the grunt with which it was usually met.

'The other slight problem was maintaining diplomatic relations with the regime the other side of the river. At the top level they were satisfactory, but when it came to the professional — gamekeeper — level, they became rather strained. Tom had the advantage in three ways: he was a Welshman, his successor was not; he knew his ground, his successor did not; he had forty years' keepering experience, his successor had not.

'On our first day's shooting, Tom had a good many of his opponent's (as he regarded the usurping Llandrog keeper) pheasants lured to his side of the river. The new man, until he realised that he had to get up earlier in the morning on our shooting days, not unnaturally resented watching his birds being brought down in front of his eyes. It was only my intervention that prevented diplomatic relationships being broken off altogether. Even so, all future negotiations had to be conducted at ministerial level.

'Tom and I had known each other far too long for these little local difficulties to dent our relationship. If he got his own way I took it in good part, it was the easier option; if I got my way he grunted and accepted the situation — for as long as it took him to alter it to his own satisfaction. Either way he usually managed to conceal the full range of his emotions from me beneath either a grunt or a smile.

'I only saw Tom Parry lose control of his emotions on one occasion. He had a big black labrador dog called Bryn, an unlovable-looking creature with the physique of a Rottweiler. Tom was a professional who regarded his dog as a tool of the trade: it either did what he wanted or it went; one did not ask where. I think he kept this particular dog to deter poachers. I never saw Bryn's temperament put to the test, but in appearance alone he certainly deterred me.

'It was early one spring when I came across Tom walking down the lane, gun under his arm, Bryn at his heel, presumably in search of vermin of one kind or another. There was something I wanted to talk to him about, so I parked the car and joined him. I said I'd walk a little way with him. We walked on, me doing most of the talking, Tom grunting occasionally.

'We were coming to a bend in the lane. I can remember the exact spot; Bryn had dropped behind to relieve himself against a stone gatepost. At that moment a hare came round the bend at full tilt in the manic way the animals behave at this time of year. It shot past us, and we looked round. The hare was on the same side of the lane as Bryn, who was balanced on three legs pumping away at the stone gatepost, his eyes fixed and his mind presumably occupied with the pleasing sensation of relief. The sex-crazed hare shot beneath the dog's uplifted leg, there was a yelp of dismay, and Bryn went sprawling over into the middle of the lane.

'I had watched this accident about to happen in sheer amazement, not believing that it actually would happen. Then I heard a gurgling sound from beside me. I looked round at Tom, who was literally doubled up with laughter. Not great guffaws, but internal rumblings that he could not control. His whole body shook. Then he straightened up, "What a strange thing to 'appen," he said.

'Tom hated cats. There is an illustration in the old Badminton Library book on shooting, of a pot-hatted, mutton-chop - whiskered gamekeeper standing in front of his vermin gibbet laden with the decaying corpses of magpies, stoats and weasels, holding up a cat by the scruff of the neck with one hand, his other fist clenched a foot from pussy's surprised-looking face. By the look on the keeper's face there can be little doubt that the cat is about to join the others on the gibbet. The caption beneath: "A Real Poacher". A generation later, a different face, and it could be Tom Parry.

'Any cat that strayed into Tom's coverts was a dead cat — sooner or later.

'I am not a cat-lover myself, but when I went to the village shop and saw, as I occasionally did, pinned up outside, notices like, "Lost, Timmy a tabby cat, last seen..." I feared for Timmy's continued existence. And though they might have been my pheasant chicks that Timmy was after, I felt a certain twinge of sympathy for Timmy's owner — imagining some old maiden lady — knowing that Tom could be on Timmy's tracks. But I said nothing. Tom had no such finer feelings; the only good cat to him was a dead cat. And thereby hangs the final irony of this tale.

'Tom Parry died quite suddenly. No lingering illness for him. If he could, he'd have been in his coverts until The Almighty's great retrievers came to pick him up. As it was he died in bed overnight. He was buried in the graveyard at Wyddgrub, the nearest village a couple of miles or so from Llandrog, and, as I remember Tom, I will also remember his funeral. Not that I wouldn't remember it anyway, as you would the final parting with an old friend, but something quite out of the ordinary occurred; uncanny almost, if you knew about Tom's aversion to cats, and most people attending his funeral did know.

'But before telling you about what happened at Tom Parry's funeral, I must tell you first something that occurred beforehand, something that did not register – until afterwards.

'Mrs Jones, the wife of the man who used to look after the graveyard at Wyddgrub, had a cat of which she was very fond; it was a black tomcat called Dai, Do or Dai as he was known in the village. She and her husband lived in a cottage fifty yards or so from the chapel, and the graveyard lay immediately behind on a square of open ground surrounded on three sides by a yew hedge. A month or so before Tom died, Dai went missing. A notice appeared in the village shop, enquiries were made, but there was no trace of the cat. I saw the notice in the shop, thought of Tom, and as usual said nothing.

'When the day of Tom Parry's funeral came, I had forgotten all about the Jones's cat.

'I don't suppose any of you have ever been to a Welsh chapel funeral; I can tell you it is a melancholy affair, not that any funeral isn't melancholy enough, but the Welsh people have a special feel for a funeral. The trappings are kept to a minimum, but the emotions come out in words and song; you do not have to understand the words – and there are plenty of them – to sense the emotion.

'After all the words were spoken, and the hymns sung at Tom Parry's funeral, we went out into the graveyard at the back of the chapel, behind us the village street, smoke hanging low over the slate roofs of the cottages, and in the distance the Cambrian Mountains. The coffin was placed on boards over the open grave, the bearers on either side holding the straps, ready to lower it into the earth. The minister and the chief mourners took up their positions, the rest of us ranged in a crescent behind. All was ready for the burial.

'The minister was about to open his mouth to say the final words, when a big black cat came loping across the turf straight towards the grave. As the animal approached its pace quickened; it did not deviate from its course until, with a bound, it was on top of the coffin. There it did pause, for what must have been only a few seconds, and I distinctly remember the yellow irises of its eyes looking balefully at us. Then the cat was gone. I did not see where it went.

'There was absolute silence for a few moments, which was ended only by whispers, coughing and the rustling of clothes, then the minister resumed the words of the committal service.

'When the burial was finished, and everybody was walking back towards the village street, the pent up silence gave way to an excited buzz of conversation, mostly in Welsh. But one old woman addressed me directly. "That cat that jumped on Tom Parry's coffin was never Dai, Mrs Jones's cat. Dai had a patch of white on the front of him. I ought to know, I seen 'im outside my back door often enough".'

97

Chapter Eleven

The Two Letters

Julian Greengrass was a man in his late forties, I guessed, fair-haired, with the sort of face people respond to by saying 'Haven't I met you somewhere before?' As he got up from behind the big desk and walked towards me with an outstretched hand and an engaging smile, the severely dressed attractive lady who had ushered me in enquired, 'Coffee or tea, Sir?' I chose coffee, and she left, closing the door silently behind her. 'It is very good of you to come,' said Mr. Greengrass, 'I hope I made it clear that you should do so entirely at your own convenience, and maybe you can have some lunch with me after we've completed our little bit of business; in fact, it involves no more than me handing a letter to you, which in accordance with the late Major Brewster's instructions perhaps you will be kind enough to open in my presence.'

Mr Greengrass indicated two armchairs in one corner of the room; I moved to one of them, whilst he returned to his desk, and extracted from one of the drawers a long buff-coloured envelope of the sort which only lawyers seem to use.

I slit open the buff envelope, extracted the letter on a single sheet of writing-paper headed Cranworth House, Flixby, Lincolnshire, and dated the 21st of October, 1986; five years and one month ago, almost to the day.

I read the letter.

Dear Harry,

You will have been handed this letter by Julian Greengrass, a partner in the family firm of solicitors, Greengrass and Writtle. His father, John Greengrass, was a brother officer of mine during the war, and we became the closest of friends. Together we shared a great deal of danger and discomfort. We spent many hours discussing what we would do when it was all over. As you know, I am a man of simple tastes, and so was John. We agreed that one of life's great pleasures was a good day's shooting with half a dozen friends on a cold bright December day; afterwards, tea with buttered toast and fruit cake, bath, change, then dinner without having to go anywhere or do anything but sit there and enjoy it.

John Greengrass was killed the week before the war in North-West Europe ended.

When I inherited Cranworth from my uncle and was able to ask some of my friends to shoot, I often thought of John and how much he would have enjoyed being with us. As you know, in order to keep the shoot going I had eventually to let two or three days each season. On the whole the guns I got on let days were not a bad crowd. But there seemed to be something missing. I thought at first it was the familiarity which goes with knowing one another well, but I came to the conclusion that what stood in the way of shared pleasure and friendly rivalry was oneupmanship. It also seemed a good many of them wanted to turn a day's shooting into a board meeting.

What had become of John Greengrass's and my wartime dream! After a particularly tiresome let day, culminating in one of the guns remarking to another in my hearing that if there was a guaranteed bag he expected enough birds to fly where he could hit them, I thought I would indulge myself in a little day-dreaming. I have never written anything before except letters and reports, but I had this feeling I wanted to spit out in words where I thought shooting was going wrong. I chose John as my stalking horse. I enclose the story I wrote.

I hope by now you and a few friends will have settled down to a pleasant dinner together each year. Before you all clean your guns for the last time, you may care to spare a thought for the state in which you will leave shooting for the next generation to inherit.
Yours ever,
Stuffy

There were a dozen or so folded pages accompanying the letter. I said to Julian Greengrass, 'Do you want me to read all this now?'

He replied, 'The instructions in Major Brewster's will were to hand you that letter as soon as it was conveniently possible five years following the anniversary of his death, and that you should open it in my presence. There is another letter which I am instructed to retain for a further six months, and then to open myself. I have no idea of the contents, as indeed I have none of the one which is now in your hands.'

'Did you know Arthur Brewster yourself?'

'Only that he was a friend of my father's, and an occasional client of the firm. His day-to-day legal affairs were handled by a firm of solicitors in Lincoln from whom we received instructions. I never knew my father either; he was killed during the war before I was born.'

'I think you should see this letter,' I said, handing it to him. 'If I may I will read the enclosure in my own time.' Julian Greengrass read the letter and handed it back to me. 'Shall we go out to lunch?' he said.

I did not read Stuffy Brewster's story in the train; with the hurly-burly of jostling commuters it did not seem the right place for joint communication. Here is what I read later that night.

1992

'You can go where you like,' said the Archangel in Charge of Time Travel, 'you have a roving commission for your mission on behalf of Saint Hubert. You will be given temporary human status, but your presence will go unrecognised by those still in the flesh. If you want to get in touch, there are call boxes in all the churches, but these should only be used in case of emergency. I have cleared any spirit movements in the area where you are likely to be operating, so there should be no problem there. You will not be able to communicate directly in any way; any urgent message to the living will be strictly through me. I have allocated you thirty human days for your mission. At the conclusion you must return here and apply for an extension, if you need one. Now, are there any questions?'

John Greengrass had no questions, and in due course departed on the mission referred to by the Archangel.

But what was that mission? Saint Hubert had explained it succinctly enough.

'I am, as you may know, adviser on field sports to the Earthly Activities Committee of which Saint Peter is the chairman' said the Saint, thoughtfully toying with the golden stag in his hand. 'His Holiness is concerned about reports coming in to him from those recently earthbound that shooting, which he intended should be a sport, is becoming a business. His Holiness may soon feel obliged to intercede. But first he would like an updated report. I have undertaken to provide this for him, and I would like you to help me in gathering information. In due course you will be provided with the necessary credentials. Now please take your rest.'

John had taken his rest, and after his briefing by the Archangel in Charge of Time Travel, had descended to Earth. Here he was woken from a deep and refreshing sleep to experience the frenetic strife of life on Earth in 1992. It was like a nightmare in reverse. He was acutely aware of the short time he had in which to complete his mission. He did not want to apply for an extension — it would be a confession of failure — he wanted to get back to rest in peace.

Temporary human status, the Archangel had said. John Greengrass supposed that meant he would repossess his old body, which did not seem to matter much because no one would be able to see it anyway. More important, would he repossess the mind and memory that went with it? But the Archangelship of Time Travel had done their work thoroughly, and he was not aware of any lack of retrieval from the memory which had served him during his lifetime.

John Greengrass's memory returned to him on the steps of Saint Paul's Cathedral, where he found himself with the great bell of the clock booming out above him. He shook himself like a dog coming out of the water; at least, it felt like that as he took in the familiar but unaccustomed surroundings. He counted the strokes, twelve of them. The sun was shining. He knew where he was, but he had no idea what he was going to do next. It was a situation in which he had often found himself before, but in different circumstances. Then for some reason he remembered that oft repeated maxim of his old friend Stuffy Brewster, 'Time spent in reconnaissance is seldom wasted'. He had not been able to do one before, so he had better get on with it now.

But what was he reconnoitring here in the City of London which had anything to do with shooting? He was confused, jet-lagged (my description, not his) by Time Travel. His mind was clearing, but he needed to think, and to plan. Then another of Stuffy's favourite military dictums came to him: the first thing to do is establish a firm base. He would establish a firm base here in London. After his long repose John was pleased with the progress he was making. He set off in the direction of the City.

So much had changed since he was last here. He was bewildered by the hurrying crowds. Where had all the bowler hats gone, and the umbrellas? John was thankful that he could choose his own route as he slid through the throng. As for the traffic, he knew he was safe from impact but instinctively avoided contact. It was not long before he felt completely overwhelmed by the crowds and the traffic, and turned into the quieter side roads to recover his self-possession. He walked on slowly, getting a grip of himself, finding time now to observe his surroundings with some degree of interest. Surely this square in which he found himself was familiar? He glanced up as he turned into it and read, Finsbury Square.

An idea had come to him. He strode out more purposefully, leaving the square by one road, turning into another, then pausing for a moment to get his bearings, and walked on again, until he came to the place he was looking for. He glanced up at the familiar façade to read the words he knew were there, Drill Hall. It was where he had enlisted at the outbreak of war. This will do me for a firm base, he said to himself. And firm base established, John Greengrass continued with his reconnaissance.

There were difficulties, to begin with. One particularly nasty moment came during a visit to a newsagents. He had gone there early in the day when the shop had just opened and there were not many people about, to read up all he could before taking to the field, but being occupied with what he was reading, he failed to notice another browser. He saw the man glance up rather guiltily from the magazine he was looking at, then the eyes dilated and the jaw fell as he gazed in Greengrass's direction. The copy of *Playboy* dropped to the floor and the man fled. It was only then it struck John that he too might have looked the same way if he had seen an open copy of *Shooting Times* apparently suspended in mid-air.

From the very beginning, John found it rather strange that Saint Hubert had chosen high summer to send him on his mission. He assumed the Saint had his reasons, a test of initiative perhaps, or Saint Peter calling for the report early; one did not question the wisdom of saints. But it did seem strange.

Then he read the following in one of the magazines, 'Her Majesty the Queen has graciously offered Sandringham House as the venue for the 1992 Game Fair which opens on the 27th of July. Her Majesty wished to emphasise the sense of occasion there is in the creation of the Single European Market, and its relevance to the traditional sports of the English countryside. Our European partners in this dynamic entrepreneurial market will have an opportunity of bringing their own sporting cultures to display at the Queen's country home in Norfolk.'

Indeed, one did not question the wisdom of saints.

John had not been to a Game Fair before, so he did not quite know what to expect. Certainly he did not expect this vast concourse of people. And the endless rows of cars. Where did they all come from? Could so many people be interested in hunting, or shooting, or fishing? He stationed himself in the ticket tent, and surreptitiously whisked away one of the programmes. It felt more like a paperback book than a programme. He leafed through the pages. So this is a Game Fair, said John to himself; my word, things have come on a bit since my day. He noted there was to be a pageant depicting European hunting techniques over the centuries to the present day, and though it was not strictly in accordance with his brief, he thought it would be interesting to watch that. The Italian Carabinieri were giving a musical ride in the main ring later that morning, and the Duc de Muscadet's Boar Hounds were parading first, then running a drag through the park. It all looked very interesting, but John could not help remembering Saint Hubert's words: 'His Holiness is concerned that shooting, which he intended should be a sport, is becoming a business.' Hunting and fishing too, it seemed.

John Greengrass moved from the tent amongst the motley in the sunshine outside. The rank and file of the crowd were unlikely looking countrymen in their leisure wear, wives wearing printed cotton dresses or thin blouses and tight trousers; couples with children in tow, either fractious or inquisitive. Striding more purposefully through this slow-moving throng, in undress uniform of ribboned panama hat, tie, shirtsleeves rolled down, and fawn trousers, were the obvious members of the field-sports brigade. John had no difficulty in recognising them. Some wore badges by which to be recognised. Then, despite the heat of the day, there were those who dressed the part, in plus-fours or deerstalker hats, or both. The scene so far reminded John of Epsom Downs on Derby Day.

Passing the gaily striped umbrellas shading the chairs and tables outside the mock-up of a typical French auberge, advertised as such by a sign with the picture of a red-legged partridge painted on it, and bearing the legend beneath, Le Perdrix Français, there was not a beret or a glass of absinthe to be seen. Rather was John Greengrass reminded of a Surrey pub back-garden at Sunday lunchtime in the summer.

At that moment there was a flourish of music from the Grand Ring, and the mounted Carabinieri titupped in to the strains of Verdi. 'Are those the Queen's huntsmen?' a four-year-old asked his mother within John's hearing. 'No dear, they're Italian policemen.' You couldn't beat the English at pageantry, but trust the Italians to create a ballet with a cast of mounted policemen. He moved away towards the main aisle of trade stands.

'Infosport: The Field Sportsman's Information Centre' read the banner outside a large candy-striped marquee, 'It's our business to find your sport. Come inside for a free consultancy.' This looked a good start. John Greengrass went inside.

The interior of the tent was a veritable masterpiece of design in canvas. There were a number of booths each with a headboard describing the area of interest to today's sportspeople. John Greengrass stopped by the booth labelled 'Hunting Tuition'. There were two or three black-leather-and-chromium-plate armchairs, a coffee table loaded with sales literature, and display boards round the sides. Behind a glass-topped desk sat a well-groomed woman.

She was listening to an earnest young man asking questions about how to pass the Hunting Test which had apparently now been introduced and standardised throughout Europe. 'Yes,' replied the consultant lady, 'we offer a correspondence course which covers the syllabus. You can enrol here, and test questions with model answers will be sent to your home address. We find most people have difficulty with Defunct Quarry Treatment and Evisceration. Hunting Law is a bit of a problem too, because it varies so much between the Chasse Communale in France and the Deutscher Jagdschutz Verband in Germany, especially now that Germany is reunited. You have to have a working knowledge of the law in all the EC countries, you see. The only one where there isn't much of a problem is Italy.' She added hopefully: 'By the way, if you wanted to go there on our Rentashoot scheme, you don't need a certificate in the former communist European countries.'

John Greengrass found it very frustrating having to rely on other people's conversation for the answers to the questions which had formed in his mind. It meant having to eavesdrop for quite some time before his question came up for answer.

The consultant lady continued on the theme of the test. 'We have qualified instructors who can help with your Practical. It's just a matter of making an appointment, and one of our boys or girls will take you through the test at our Hunting Centre in your area.'

John wandered round looking at the various displays.

Under the heading 'Quarry Evisceration and Preparation' there was a pictorial step-by-step guide to drawing and plucking a pheasant. Beneath, the pheasant plucker was cautioned, 'All game for sale must conform to EC regulations for inspection and treatment. A detailed leaflet is available'. Another poster dealt with the hunter's social responsibilities, including: minimum wages for hunting staff, grievance procedure, wearing of safety equipment, ecologically acceptable ammunition, and respect for rural inhabitants. Again, a leaflet and advice was available from Infosport.

On the way out of the Infosport tent he paused at 'Rentashoot Computer Service', another booth in the canvas complex, and with an array of video screens. 'Key in your requirements,' an assistant said to a prospective client, 'and we can provide you with anything from reindeer stalking in Scotland to a wolf hunt in Poland. We provide instruction, plus of course all the equipment you need. What is your particular interest, Sir?' 'Football,' the man replied.

Once more out in the sunshine John Greengrass set off to find Gunmakers' Row. His remit from Saint Hubert was to report on shooting, and he had no intention of getting sidetracked; nevertheless, the report must be balanced and take account of all the circumstances: the software as well as the hardware. He must keep his eye open for evidence of trends, of fashions – not that he was much of an observer of that scene – and of attitudes.

John Greengrass was aroused from this reverie by a large man wearing a deerstalker hat bearing down on him. He instinctively stepped to one side and the man passed through his left shoulder. He remembered where he was and what he was supposed to be doing. There across the aisle was an open-sided tent displaying sportswear and accessories. He would have a look inside.

He was careful not to pick anything up, but plenty of other people were doing that, so he had a chance to see all he wanted. One man was trying on a coat, all zips and padding, with 'Top Gun' embroidered over the left breast pocket. A streamer surmounting a rack of ties announced, 'Why not have your own designer-crafted syndicate tie?' On a clothes rack labelled, 'Hunter Recognition Shot-Resistant' hung padded waistcoats with fluorescent panels front and back.

The range of headgear included everything from deerstalkers ('As worn in the Scots Highlands') to pot-shaped long-peaked caps ('American Hunting Caps') so favoured by baseball players and the American armed forces.

Having seen enough of clothes he moved on to the display cabinets. Here, amongst 'Essential Hunting Equipment' were knives, 'For Bleeding The Quarry' it said underneath, and gadgets of all kinds. One ingenious device was called a 'Hit Recorder'. According to the sales literature, it (a slim plastic tube) clipped to the side of the barrels just in front of the fore-end. Each time the gun was fired the device registered. If a hit was scored a touch of the finger notched it up. After the shooting was over you inserted the cylinder in a container the size of a cigarette packet, and got a tiny printout showing the ratio of hits to misses. 'Prove your point,' the leaflet said, 'by handing this to the person who asks you how you got on last drive.'

There was also a portable telephone carrier, in canvas, or 'Executive Style' in real leather.

At that moment he heard a fusillade of shots from the direction of the Grand Ring, and the voice of the announcer giving his jolly gung-ho commentary. 'And that, ladies and gentlemen, is the conclusion of the German *ring-jagd*. The local hunters started by forming a circle in the forest, nearly a mile in diameter perhaps, and now as they converge the game is driven towards the centre. When the quarry is surrounded, the chief huntsman blows his horn. All the other hunters face about and fire as the quarry breaks out from the constricting circle.' John Greengrass wondered what happened to those on the other side of the constricting circle if some of the hunters forgot to face about when they heard the chief huntsman's horn. Or did not even hear it. His thoughts were drowned as all the hunters joined in Weber's 'Huntsman's Chorus' to the accompaniment of the Band of The Grenadier Guards.

Passing 'Gundogs', he noted with interest a show-card which announced, 'The Combidog. Hunter, Pointer, and Retriever: the result of years of canine genetic engineering'. He did not see the actual dog, so he couldn't imagine what the animal looked like.

'Now thrive the armourers'; Italian and Spanish. But what of the English? Here he was at Gunmakers' Row. John Greengrass slipped from one retailer's display of weaponry to the next, each containing a bewildering variety of the basic twelve-bore shotgun, now described as the calibre 18.5-mm smoothbore. Over-and-under, side-by-side, ribs swamped, single, raised, ventilated, smooth, cross-milled or file-cut, stocks straight-hand, half or full pistol grip, combs sloping or Monte Carlo, recoil pads or composition heel-plates, fore-ends splinter, schnozzle, or beaver-tail. He read the descriptions without knowing what they meant.

Apparently the few English armourers that still thrived did not find it necessary to come to the Fair. John Greengrass supposed that they had no need to tout for trade when they already had full order books. Besides, some might not wish to advertise in the grounds of their most valued customer. The classic lines of the 'Best London Gun' were therefore only to be seen in imitation. If you were rich enough to afford the real thing, you ordered it in London. That presumably was the thinking which explained the absence of 'carriage-trade' English gunmakers.

Further along the Row, a plain sign outside a green-and-white-striped tent modestly advertised 'Pierre Lapin, Gunmaker, London and Paris'. The tent front looked somehow different, more restrained, than many of its strident neighbours. Perhaps it was this that made John Greengrass interested to see what was inside. He entered. In terms of the overcrowded displays he had so far seen the interior was in total contrast. The rectangle of bare white canvas was softened by drapes of hessian, deep shades of green and brown, softly lit from within. A carpet was on the floor. There was a complete absence of the usual rows of gun-racks, counters and overcrowded shelving. Instead there was just one large glass-topped display case in the middle attended by a tall man in a pink shirt, foulard tie, and lightweight dark blue trousers. A table spread with an immaculate white cloth occupied one corner, on it were a range of bottles, some in coolers, a variety of glasses, and an ice bucket. In another corner stood two comfortable-looking armchairs with a low table between them.

The tall man — obviously the proprietor — was engaged in conversation with the half-dozen or so other occupants of the tent. He was saying, by way of explanation to a question that he had been asked, 'Yes, I came from Paris to work with one of your famous gunmakers in London. After a few years I decided to leave to start my own business. To me, you see, creating a gun is an art form, but one needs first to learn the

109

craft. Now I challenge what few London gunmakers you have left. Come, look.' He led the group from the table where they had been standing, over to the display case. John Greengrass followed. The Frenchman flicked a switch, and the interior was lit up. There on deep purple silk lay a pair of assembled guns which were truly magnificent in their slender design, a contrast of shining metal and figured walnut, and finely engraved gold and silver lock-plates. 'I call them the 18.5-millimetre Presidential,' said their creator.

'If you are very rich I can make a pair for you,' continued Monsieur Lapin, 'but they will cost you a great deal of money, and take two years to complete. But soon I hope to produce a simple well-made gun at a more modest price. Maybe I will call this The Citizen or even The Republican,' he added with a little laugh. 'But by then my name will be known in London, and I will not have to come to your Game Fair.'

Craftsmanship is alive and well and living in France, thought John Greengrass to himself as he slipped out of the tent, but really I could never have had a Pierre Lapin 18.5-millimetre. Not while I could have had a Holland and Holland or a Purdey twelve-bore.

After the cool interior of M. Lapin's tent, the sunshine and the crowds made him feel suddenly tired. He was not used to this sort of razzmatazz, and he wanted to rest. Come to think of it, he had seen just about enough of the 1992 Game Fair, and what he had seen had not favourably impressed him. Overt commercialism, crowds of people who either knew nothing of field sports, or the few who by the look of them thought they knew everything. Was this gathering really typical of people who enjoyed sport in the English countryside? As for our European partners bringing their own sporting cultures to display...! Behind the tent containing Dogextras Electronic Collars and Training Aids, he lay down for a bit of a rest.

The trouble with temporary human status, John Greengrass thought to himself, is that one gets all the disadvantages and none of the advantages. The sooner I get this investigation over with the better. He rose to his feet and started walking in the direction of the car parks, intending to pick the most comfortable lift he could back to London.

He was nearing the end of the rows of trade stands, and the crowd was beginning to thin into a trickle, when he saw a figure which for some reason or another magnetised his attention. The man was walking ahead of him in the same direction, coatless, shirtsleeves rolled down, linen trousers, panama hat; nothing to distinguish him from hundreds of men John had seen that day. And yet John Greengrass had a strong feeling of recognition. He wanted to go up and say, 'Do tell me your name, I'm sure we know one another'.

The man turned into a stand, one of the last in the aisle. John followed him. The words of the Archangel in Charge of Time Travel came back to him, 'Any urgent message to the living will be strictly through me'. All very well, he thought, but what about messages from the living, they can hardly get through to the Archangel, and yet I am certain this chap has got a message for me if he only knew I was here. What is it?

Inside the booth there was a single table with some literature displayed on it. The man picked up one of the leaflets and began to read. John stood impotently by. The attendant in charge, who had presumably been outside in the sun, came in. 'Can I help you, Sir?' he said. The man looked up, and for the first time John Greengrass saw his face. It greatly reminded him of what his own image in the looking-glass had once been like. That much recall and that much only was allowed by the Archangel in Charge of Time Travel. John was released from the spell, and walked out of the tent.

He glanced back, and for the first time noticed the banner over the entrance. It read, 'Society For The Restoration Of Rural Sport In England.'

I folded up the sheets of paper, replaced them, together with Stuffy Brewster's letter, in the original envelope which Julian Greengrass had handed me that morning, and put the long, stiff buff envelope in that drawer of my desk which is mentally labelled pending; in other words, the contents are to be thought about — and thought about. I went to bed, tired after my day in London; my wife was already asleep. I thought about the contents of that long buff envelope, of how I had received it, and the message it contained which as yet was not entirely clear to me, of Julian Greengrass and of his dead father John resurrected in Stuffy Brewster's imagination. And then I went to sleep.

I must be honest. I thought less about the long buff envelope and its contents in my pending drawer the following day, and each succeeding day as the events in my humdrum existence took over: what to do about this problem, getting ready for that engagement, or wrestling with one or another of the crowded thoughts of everyday living. Yet the letter and Stuffy's story stayed with me, to intrude, not just when I opened the pending drawer and saw the long buff envelope sitting there, but occasionally when my thoughts ranged beyond my own little local problems and pleasures.

What had Stuffy intended by the rather cumbersome manner in which his letter and the John Greengrass story had come into my hands? Surely it was something more than just a protest against the way he saw his favourite sport being manipulated. But for the life of me I could not fathom out what had been on his mind when he arranged this uncharacteristic little epilogue. At least it had brought me into contact with Julian Greengrass, whom I liked instinctively.

Our next Gunroom dinner, due in six weeks' time, spurred me into doing something positive about the contents of that long buff envelope. I asked Julian Greengrass as a guest. I also read out Stuffy's letter after dinner, and although I did not read the story as well — after-dinner reading palls — I paraphrased it as best I could. The coincidence of where we were, and of John Greengrass's firm base on Earth, was not lost either on his son, or on the rest of us round the table. When I had finished speaking, there were a few moments' silence. Then someone said, 'Do you suppose Arthur Brewster felt he had left some unfinished business when he wrote that?'

Next time I opened my pending drawer, I took out the long buff envelope and laid it to rest at the bottom of the box file bearing the label 'Gunroom'.

It must have been at least two or three months later when I had a telephone call from Julian Greengrass, 'You remember I told you,' he said, 'that I had a further letter sent to me in accordance with Major Brewster's will, which I was to open in six months' time and act upon myself? Well, I have opened the letter, and I think you ought to see the contents. I am sending you a copy. Perhaps we could talk about it when you are next in London.'

The following day another of those long buff envelopes arrived. I opened it, took out the photostated copy of the letter inside, again headed Cranworth House, Flixby, and read:

Dear Julian,
I presume only on my friendship with your father to address you by your Christian name, because we have never met. When your father was killed in the last days of the war, and you were not yet born, a light went out in my life; I felt there was no way I could rekindle it by contacting your mother. We had shared the pleasure of your father's company in different ways. In my defence it could be said my friendship with him was forged in wartime; I have no doubt it would have been formed and tempered by our common interests when peace came; furthermore it would have brought me in contact with your mother and yourself. But it was not to be.

Now that I am an old bachelor, I know I made a mistake to live on memories of the dead and to do nothing about the living; your father was dead, but he had left you as a legacy.

113

And I never bothered to discover you. Until it was nearly too late. But not quite.

Had your father survived the war, we might have enjoyed together some of the pleasures — shooting amongst them — which the sophisticated world of the late twentieth century has sought to remodel. As it is I am glad he keeps his memories intact. They focus sharply when you live with danger and discomfort. Of course there is change in all things, it is called progress. But forty-five years on, what changes are for the better, and what for the worse? And what progress has been made in shooting for the sport of it?

If I have not done a great deal of good during my lifetime, I hope I have not done much harm. Give and take; that is the name of the game for most of us, yet I have the feeling I have taken more than I have given. The one thing I did not take was a wife, thinking that marriage would interfere with my freedom, when a lady I loved nearly as much as my shooting gave me the chance. She was wise enough to sense my reluctance and withdrew from further contact. I was not given a second chance. So now at the end of the day I have a fuller pocket and an emptier heart. A heart not quite empty though, there are my friends. And you, the son of the friend with whom I shared the most. Surely you should inherit some of my worldly goods in place of the wife I never wed, and the child I never had.

I have instructed my solicitors in Lincoln to make available to you a sum of ten thousand pounds. I have also tried to arrange matters so that you will have had a chance of meeting some of my friends, whom I believe share the same values and interests as I have done, and your father as well. Take the money on trust, Julian Greengrass, a trust not accountable to the law but to the memory of your father, and use it how you think best. I promise neither he nor I will come back to Earth to check up on how you have spent it.

Yours ever,
Arthur Brewster.

I rang Julian Greengrass the following morning to thank him for sending me a copy of the letter.

'Quite a tall order, isn't it?' he said.

'Yes,' I replied, 'rather more difficult than the task he left behind for me.'